Social and therapeutic horticulture:

Evidence and messages from research

Joe Sempik, Jo Aldridge and Saul Becker

Thrive, in association with the Centre for Child and Family Research, Loughborough University

First published in Great Britain in 2003 by Thrive in association with the Centre for Child and Family Research, Loughborough University.

Thrive

The Geoffrey Udall Centre, Beech Hill, Reading RG7 2AT

Tel: 0118 9885688

www.thrive.org.uk

Centre for Child and Family Research

Department of Social Sciences, Loughborough University, Leicestershire LE11 3TU

Tel: 01509 228355

www.ccfr.org.uk

Printed by Media Services, Loughborough University.

Further copies of this report are available from Thrive.

© Thrive and CCFR 2003

ISBN 0 907274 29 3

Acknowledgements

This document was prepared by the Research Team at Loughborough University as part of the 'Growing Together' project funded by the National Lottery Community Fund. "Growing Together – Promoting Social Inclusion, Health and Well-being for Vulnerable Adults through the use of Horticulture and Gardening" is a collaboration between Loughborough University and the charity Thrive.

The authors acknowledge the co-operation and collaboration of our colleagues at Thrive, especially Tim Spurgeon and Louise Finnis.

We would also like to thank the consultants on the project for their help and advice in the preparation of this document: John Ferris, Carol Norman and Bill Silburn.

We would like to acknowledge the Community Fund for the financial support of this project under grant number RG 10024093.

Photographs by Jamie Finlay.

Further information about this project is available on:

www.growingtogether.org.uk

Contents

1 Introduction

Horticulture[1], in many different forms, has been used as a therapy or as an adjunct to therapy in the treatment of disease. It has also been used to achieve social and psychological benefit for disadvantaged individuals and communities and has been used to promote health, and physical and psychological well-being. Consequently there is a large descriptive literature on horticulture, health and well-being much of which, however, assumes that the benefits of horticulture are implicit and detailed evidence is not cited.

When Markee and Janick (1979) carried out a major search of the literature published between 1970 and 1978 they uncovered 213 references but they noted:

> "The high number of articles in this field was entirely unexpected. However, our analysis of the references indicated that most are 'paraprofessional', with few if any experimental data. We were surprised to discover that a field where so little experimental evidence is available is able to generate so much literature. It seems clear that the concept of horticultural therapy is in itself sufficiently intriguing to generate a great deal of interest and activity. We conclude, assuming our bibliography 1970-1978 is representative, that more hard information is needed on efficacy of horticultural therapy" (Markee and Janick, 1979, p. 694).

At around the same time Morreau (1979, quoted in, Ackley and Cole, 1987) made a similar observation but perhaps more poetically:

> "The philosophy underlying the field has endured for thousands of years, thereby standing the test of time. The specialized terminology has existed for approximately 30 years, and the pedagogy for teaching has been established for about 10 years. What doesn't appear to be available is solid documentation as to the effectiveness of the therapeutic process" (Morreau, 1979, in: Ackley and Cole, 1987, p. 70).

To our knowledge a literature search on the scale of Markee and Janick's has not been carried out since. The purpose of our review is to gather published data from the literature which would provide scientific evidence for the benefits of horticulture. Almost a quarter of a century has passed since the comments shown above were made and an examination of the literature would also show whether they were still valid today. Another purpose of this review is to bring together the literature on social and therapeutic horticulture as an introduction to those who are unfamiliar with the subject. This task has been made easier by the work of researchers such as Diane Relf who have not only produced reviews of the subject but have acted as editors for conference and symposium proceedings (see Appendix 2).

---

[1] The terms 'gardening' and 'horticulture' are frequently used interchangeably and this can cause confusion. Although the word 'horticulture' is derived from the Latin 'hortus' (garden) and 'cultura' (culture) literally meaning the cultivation of a garden it now has a wider meaning. Horticulture encompasses the art and science of plant care, propagation and study.

Methods

Many of the volumes of collected papers, conference proceedings and text books were known to the authors and provided leads for references which could be followed.

Researchers with known interests in the field of social and therapeutic horticulture were contacted and some were also able to provide leads. Electronic databases of published material were used to search for keywords and known authors and these are shown in Appendix 1.

Over 1,000 titles were viewed (because of overlap, i.e. the same titles appearing on different databases, it is not possible to determine the exact number) and over 300 of these were placed on a Microsoft *Access* database especially constructed for the purpose. References were selected and read where the title or keywords suggested evidence of the benefits of social and therapeutic horticulture or description of the processes involved. These were analysed further and classified according to subject matter.

This analysis of the literature is based on 131 references of which 73 are directly concerned with the use of social and therapeutic horticulture. Of these 73 articles, 26 were classed as purely 'descriptive' and contained no actual quantitative[2] or qualitative[3] data. These are included here because they describe and define the practice of social and therapeutic horticulture and the benefits which have been associated with it.

The general reviews of horticultural therapy and personal reflections on horticulture and gardening are not included in this written review which attempts to present the evidence for the effectiveness of horticulture as a social and therapeutic activity and to present a model of how this process works from the available research.

The literature

The literature relevant to therapeutic horticulture can broadly be divided into three categories: the first is based around occupational therapy where horticulture is one of a number of different activities involved in rehabilitation. Much of the literature concerned with occupational therapy is in the form of practical information for practitioners and research carried out by them.

It may be useful to present a definition of occupational therapy here, this one is taken from the World Federation of Occupational Therapy (May 1989, quoted in Turner, Foster & Johnson, 1996).

> "Occupational therapy is the treatment of physical and psychiatric conditions through specific activities in order to help people reach their maximum level of function and independence in all aspects of daily life" (Turner, Foster & Johnson, 1996, p. 5).

Horticulture has been used as one of the "specific activities" mentioned above and when it is used exclusively the therapeutic process can be described as 'horticultural therapy'. However, the terms 'horticultural therapy' and 'therapeutic horticulture' are frequently used in the literature, sometimes interchangeably, to describe the process of interaction between the individual and the plants or gardens and (in most cases) facilitated by a trained practitioner. The charity Thrive uses the following definitions of Horticultural Therapy and Therapeutic Horticulture. These were agreed by practitioners at a conference on Professional Development held in September 1999:

> "Horticultural therapy is the use of plants by a trained professional as a medium through which certain clinically defined goals may be met".

> "Therapeutic horticulture is the process by which individuals may develop well-being using plants and horticulture. This is achieved by active or passive involvement" (Growth Point, 1999, p. 4).

The distinction being that horticultural therapy has a pre-defined clinical goal similar to that found in occupational therapy whilst therapeutic horticulture is

---

[2] *Quantitative: research based on analysing quantities, for example, numerical data from surveys.*
[3] *Qualitative: analysis of the meaning of events to people and their interpretations of those events, for example, through the use of in-depth interviews.*

directed towards improving the well-being of the individual in a more generalised way. This can be the attainment of employment, an increased sense of self esteem or some other perceived benefit. Perhaps the term 'social and therapeutic horticulture' best describes the process by which plants and horticulture are used to develop well-being since, as this review will show, *social* interactions and outcomes play a significant role.

The second category of the literature, that devoted specifically to horticultural therapy and therapeutic horticulture, is similar in a way to that on occupational therapy i.e. with a prescriptive practical approach and research mostly carried out by practitioners in the course of their work. It is important to remember that clinical research is both expensive and time-consuming and that to expect controlled trials of horticultural therapy in the manner of clinical trials for new drugs is entirely unrealistic. Each recorded observation, however, provides further evidence for the therapeutic benefits of horticulture.

The third category of research connected with therapeutic horticulture is that of psychology, particularly of landscape and environmental psychology and this provides its theoretical basis. Most of this work has been carried out by university staff trained in research methods and both experimental and empirical data are available to provide a mechanistic framework for horticultural therapy.

For convenience the information in this review is presented categorised according to the user group (e.g. older people, people with mental health problems, offenders etc.), however, it must be remembered that there is considerable overlap between the different groups, for example, issues of mental health overlap with those of rehabilitation and employment-creation.

Analysis of 131 texts presented in this literature review provides evidence on the outcomes and effectiveness of horticulture and gardening in a number of different therapeutic settings and with different groups of people. The review presents this evidence and draws it together to create a synthesis and a model that will help to explain the processes and outcomes. This model is presented in Section 5. While there is clear evidence that the outcomes of social and therapeutic horticulture can be positive and multifaceted, for example, in promoting health gain, general well-being, social cohesion, employment, skills development etc. there seems little doubt that this evidence base is currently under-developed and, at times, lacking in scientific rigour. Evidence can take many forms, from the anecdotal and descriptive through to rigorous academic research. This literature review draws on all these forms of evidence, but it is the evidence from systematic and analytical research which forms the best basis for the development of understanding, policy and practice. This review shows that this latter type of evidence – systematic academic inquiry – on the outcomes of social and therapeutic horticulture is limited. The underlying messages from this review concern not just the outcomes of social and therapeutic horticulture but also how fertile an area this is for future research.

2 Horticulture in rehabilitation, physical health, mental health and well-being

The role of rehabilitation is to restore a person to the quality of life and, in many cases, the employment they had prior to the illness, injury or circumstances that damaged that quality. Where this is not possible its role is to maximise the quality of life of the individual. Much of the responsibility for the promotion of rehabilitation now falls to occupational therapists.

Horticulture and physical rehabilitation

Many different activities have been used and are now used in occupational therapy and horticulture and gardening is one of those. In his book, *The Rehabilitation of the Injured*, Colson (1944) describes different gardening activities that may be used as occupational therapy. He lists "only those gardening activities which have been found of value as therapy" (p 185) so, although evidence is not presented as to the effectiveness of these activities, it is clear that they have been selected as a result of experience with patients. He grades different activities according to the level of physical exertion, so for example, hoeing, raking and pruning are graded as light work and scything and digging are heavy work. But by modifying these activities different grades can be obtained:

> "The grading suggested is not absolute for by modifying the work it is possible to change the strength of a basic occupation. For example, hoeing weeds on paths with the draw hoe is lighter work than earthing up potatoes with the same hoe" (Colson, 1944, p. 185).

Colson also lists specific gardening activities to develop movement in particular joints (pp. x-xvi).

Other textbooks on occupational therapy also describe gardening activities (see for example, Turner, Foster and Johnson, 1996, pp. 131-136). However, the activities used in occupational therapy have tended to vary according to the availability of facilities and changing attitudes. Of six other textbooks on occupational therapy which were examined (all published since 1998) only one mentioned gardening as an activity. The focus of gardening as a therapeutic activity appears to have moved towards practitioners of 'horticultural therapy' and it is not known how many occupational therapists use gardening at present.

With the development of horticultural therapy there have been many different accounts (see, for example, Simson and Straus, 1998) giving detailed descriptions of gardening and horticultural activities for rehabilitation following physical injury and illness, but there have been very few evaluations of its effectiveness. Perhaps this is due to the provenance of gardening and horticulture in early occupational therapy and therefore its acceptance as an effective form of therapy. Some studies, however, have been carried out.

Ackley and Cole (1987) evaluated a horticultural therapy programme for children with cerebral palsy.

They studied 44 institutionalised children who were assigned to either a control group or to a group receiving twenty horticultural therapy sessions over a ten week period. The children were tested using the American Association on Mental Deficiency (AAMD) Adaptive Behavior Scale for Children and Adults, a test used by hospital staff and considered to be effective in evaluating the progress of children with cerebral palsy. They found no statistically significant[4] differences between the control group and the group receiving horticultural therapy. They concluded that:

> "The results of this study indicate that a horticultural therapy program which is adjunctive in nature, of short duration, and applied by a volunteer teacher on a part-time basis may not make a significant improvement in the AAMD Adaptive Behavior Scale Part I performance of children with cerebral palsy" (Ackley and Cole, 1987, p. 72).

The authors did not recommend the abandonment of horticultural therapy, rather more research using professional staff who could work in close collaboration with other trained therapists. They suggested that the research should also be extended to groups with different levels of disability and different ages.

Case histories illustrating the use of horticultural therapy in the rehabilitation of victims of car accidents and stroke are given by Wichrowski et al (1998) and by Strauss and Gabaldo (1998). Although detailed evaluations of the role of horticultural therapy in the physical rehabilitation process were not carried out the authors report an improvement in the well-being and self-confidence (and in some cases socialisation) of the patients.

Provision of horticultural therapy also led to the development of an interest in horticulture in some of the patients and its adoption as a leisure activity or vocational goal. For example Wichrowski et al (1998) describes the case of a patient who sustained a spinal injury as a result of a road traffic accident and following a rehabilitation programme which included horticultural therapy decided to pursue a career in horticulture:

> "Bruce called again after he graduated from college. He was not that interested in a computer career, and decided to go back to school to become a landscape architect. This is a viable and realistic career choice because of the current capabilities of computers in design work. Bruce also told us he had his own greenhouse, built for him to house tanks to grow aquatic plants. He had developed a small business and was selling the plants to local nurseries.
>
> Horticultural therapy helped to change Bruce's life by offering and opening to him an achievable and emotionally and intellectually satisfying vocational future" (Wichrowski et al, 1998, p. 98).

Sarno and Chambers (1997) described a pilot horticultural therapy programme for patients with aphasia. The programme was designed to help rehabilitation by decreasing stress, increasing self esteem and providing the opportunity for patients to communicate and interact socially. The authors suggest that provision for such opportunity to communicate, under conditions which are not stressful, could encourage the patients to be more forthcoming in their speech. Although the programme was not intended as a research project and therefore data were not collected in any systematic way anecdotal evidence from the programme suggested that the intended outcomes were achieved:

> "Some of the spouses and the volunteer leaders observed that many of the individuals with aphasia appeared to do more talking while engaged in horticultural activities. One spouse indicated that houseplants became a newly shared hobby with her partner" (Sarno and Chambers, 1997, p. 89).

Some measure of the success of the programme is given by the fact that two of the participants in the

---

[4] 'Statistically significant' indicates that the calculated probability of any difference between groups occurring by chance is less than a preset level, usually 1 in 20 (0.05).

programme (out of nineteen recruited to the project) became volunteers in another horticultural project. The authors suggest that horticultural projects may be particularly suitable for patients with aphasia:

> "Most endeavors require some degree of verbal skill, and it is always a challenge to find recreational activities which are suitable for individuals with aphasia. Clearly, the nature of horticultural activities lend themselves easily to communicative disabled individuals. In the horticultural context, the lack of demand for verbal interaction reduces the burden on the disabled communicator, thereby relieving stress and facilitating relaxation and pleasure. This is believed to foster the increased talking observed by spouses and volunteers. Contact with living plants and natural materials provides soothing and comforting sensory involvement. The enjoyment and satisfaction expressed by the patients reflect this" (Sarno and Chambers, 1997, p. 89-90).

Although the above two studies were concerned with individuals with physical problems i.e. cerebral palsy and aphasia their focus was on behavioural and psychological factors. Perhaps the only evidence for the effectiveness of horticulture in physical rehabilitation lies in the experience of therapists as handed down in textbooks on occupational and horticultural therapy, rather than research based evidence.

Horticulture and mental health

In contrast to the paucity of research and evidence on the effectiveness of horticulture in improving physical health through occupational therapy there has been a great deal of work on horticulture and mental health. Gardens have been associated with both prisons and psychiatric hospitals for many years. Although their prime function has been as a source of provisions (i.e. to supply food, vegetables etc.) for these institutions their possible curative or therapeutic role has been reported over the last two hundred years.

Many authors writing about therapeutic horticulture propose Dr Benjamin Rush (1745-1813) as the 'father' of therapeutic horticulture. It is useful to consider his contribution to horticulture and mental health in the context of his writings at some length.

Benjamin Rush published 5 books in a series of *Medical Inquiries and Observations*, the last being concerned with *The Diseases of The Mind* (Rush, 1812). In this volume the practice of horticulture is mentioned twice. In the first instance as a remedy for *'hypochondriasis or tristimania'* (hypochondriasis, or as Rush prefers to call it, tristimania, is not in this case an imagined disease but an anxiety or depressive disorder). Rush writes:

> "EMPLOYMENT, or business of some kind. Man was made to be active. Even in paradise he was employed in the healthy and pleasant exercises of cultivating a garden. Happiness consisting in folded arms, and in a pensive contemplation, beneath rural shades, and by the side of purling brooks, never had any existence, except in the brains of mad poets, and love-sick girls and boys. Hypochondriac derangement has always kept pace with the inactivity of body and mind which follows wealth and independence in all countries. It is frequently induced by this cause in those citizens, who retire, after a busy life, into the country, without carrying with them a relish for agriculture, gardening, books, or literary society.

> Building, commerce, a public employment, an executorship to a will; above all, agriculture, have often cured this disease. The last, that is, agriculture, by agitating the passions by alternate hope, fear, and enjoyment, and by rendering bodily exercise or labour necessary, is calculated to produce the greatest benefit. Great care should however be taken, never to advise retirement to a part of the country where good society cannot be enjoyed upon easy terms" (Rush, 1812, pp. 117-118).

And as a remedy for *manalgia* (a disorder characterised by self neglect, "taciturnity...indifference to all surrounding objects, insensitivity to heat and cold") (Rush, 1812, p. 216):

> "Labour has several advantages over exercise, in being not only more stimulating, but more durable in its effects, whereby it is more calculated to arrest wrong habits of action, and to restore such as are regular and natural. It has been remarked, that the maniacs of the male sex in all hospitals, who assist in cutting wood, making fires, and digging in a garden, and the females who are employed in washing, ironing, and scrubbing floors, often recover, while persons, whose rank exempts them from performing such services, languish away their lives within the walls of the hospital" (Rush, 1812, p. 226).

The last sentence of the paragraph above is to be found in many texts on therapeutic horticulture and gardening. Rush then continues by describing the case history of a man who had apparently cured himself of his madness by working on the hay harvest.

> "In favour of the benefits of labour, in curing this disease, I shall select one from among many facts that might be mentioned. In the year 1801 I attended an English Gentleman, soon after his arrival in America, who was afflicted with this grade of madness. My prescriptions relieved, but did not cure him. He returned to his family in Maryland, where, in the time of hay harvest, he was allured into a meadow, and prevailed upon to take a rake into his hands, and to assist in making hay. He worked for some time, and brought on thereby a profuse sweat, which soon carried off his disease. This account of his remedy and cure I received from himself, in a very sensible letter written a few weeks after his recovery" (Rush, 1812, pp. 226-227).

Although Rush advises the use of horticulture for his patients, some of his other remedies are not so benign and include bloodletting, purges, emetics and diets (Rush, 1812, pp. 99-100). The remedies he describes were the recognised treatments of his time and Rush, himself, was firmly rooted in the thinking of the eighteenth century at a time when medical knowledge was rapidly advancing into the next century. His enthusiasm for bloodletting and his theories on the causes of insanity has led to some critical views of Rush, but it is important to note that throughout his *Medical Inquiries and Observations upon The Diseases of the Mind* Rush advocates the humane treatment of patients with the minimum of restraint or coercion at a time when the inmates of asylums were regarded by many as a legitimate form of entertainment.

In 'recent' times O'Reilly and Handforth (1955) were among the first authors to examine the value of horticulture as a therapy for psychiatric patients. They evaluated the efficacy of a horticultural programme for 14 women patients who had been considered as refractory to all forms of treatment. Of this group of patients 11 were diagnosed as schizophrenic, 1 as epileptic with behavioural problems and 2 as 'mental defectives'. O'Reilly and Handforth presented the case studies of all 14 patients and noted that:

> "Of the 14 patients who participated in our pilot project, only one has failed to show a striking degree of improvement. The other 13 are still mentally ill, but in relinquishing their positions of isolation, they have become better adapted to the hospital environment" (O'Reilly and Handforth, 1955, p. 766).

They recorded an improvement in the personal appearance and hygiene of the patients, reduced violent outbursts, increased communication and reduced isolation. The patients also became interested in the social functions of the hospital and were willing to participate in them. One brief case study illustrates the observed improvement:

"Miss M.R. – This 39-year-old schizophrenic patient has been in hospital since 1939, having become psychotic in adolescence. She continued to deteriorate in spite of physical therapies and was filthy in her habits, resistive, and destructive. In addition to exhibiting the usual schizophrenic pattern of withdrawal, she took pains never to show her face, even when eating. On the ward, she neglected her personal appearance and was never interested in any activity. Since joining the gardening group she has, for the first time in many years, become interested in something. This interest has been accompanied by an improvement in her personal appearance, and a general improvement in her habits. She no longer keeps her face covered, and is eager to go out with the group each morning" (O'Reilly and Handforth, 1955, p. 765).

The gardening programme had a cohesive effect on the dynamics of the group and where previously the patients had behaved as isolated, withdrawn individuals they began to function as a social unit:

"Whereas at first each patient went her own way, lost in her own fantasies, there has been a definite trend towards greater cohesion. Verbal and nonverbal forms of communication have increased. It is noteworthy that even on days when the weather is too bad for patients to go out, they still stick together as a group on the ward. Not only does the group hold together, but the group feeling has communicated itself to other patients on the ward, and requests to join the group are beginning to be heard" (O'Reilly and Handforth, 1955, p. 764).

Similar improvements in social functioning were observed by Prema, Devarajaiah and Gopinath (1986) in 10 male schizophrenic patients taking part in a horticulture programme in Bangalore, India. The patients volunteered their perceptions of the benefits of the programme and the authors report such comments as "able to get more friends", "had close friendship with three members" and "friendship developed" as indicators of the improved social interaction and reduced isolation of their patients. The authors note that:

"It was observed that the interactions, both frequency and intensity, improved as they continued to work together. In their interactions, they spontaneously shared their personal problems with each other. They began to learn new ways of relating to others, maintaining themselves and helping each other in the course of their work.

They were regular in their work and treatment programmes. However, they preferred to work in group rather than individually in the allotted sites. In fact, the relationship was so much strengthened that they continued their relationship outside the field also" (Prema, Devarajaiah and Gopinath, 1986, p. 156).

The importance of group dynamics was also reported recently by Perrins-Margalis et al (2000). Perrins-Margalis and his co-workers carried out a detailed study of 10 patients with chronic mental health problems in the setting of a "psychosocial/vocational rehabilitation clubhouse". The researchers participated in the horticultural activities and acted as members of the therapeutic group in order to collect data and make field notes. Semi-structured interviews[5] with all participants were carried out at the end of the six week study and each participant filled out a weekly diary relating to their horticultural experiences. The authors identified seven major themes from the data which related to their conceptual model of quality of life (as described by Zhan, 1992). These themes were:

- *The group experience: Group dynamics lead to feelings of accomplishment.*

- *The sharing experience: A self-satisfying aspect of the horticulture experience.*

- *The learning experience: The rewarding opportunity to learn new activities.*

- *The sensory experience: The contribution of*

sensory components to one's well being.

- *The creative experience: An outlet for self-expression and self concept.*
- *The emotional experience: The fun and enjoyable aspects of horticulture.*
- *The reminiscent experience: The rekindling of positive memories.*

By working within a group the participants were able to draw on each other for ideas and motivation and accomplish tasks and gain satisfaction that would otherwise not be possible:

> "The group context allowed participants to create a particular activity to their satisfaction. For participants who found it difficult to create something, it was comforting to look to other group members for ideas.

> Participants described the group as a 'team'. The group provided reinforcement for those participants who were less motivated to do the activity" (Perrins-Margalis *et al*, 2000, p. 22).

Sensory aspects of the horticultural activities, smells, colours and handling soil, were important to the participants and all commented on them. The researchers observed most of the participants in the study picking up flowers and smelling their scent.

> "It was believed that working with their hands in the soil, and viewing and smelling the brightly coloured flowers and herbs heightened the sensory experience for the horticulture group" (Perrins-Margalis *et al*, 2000, p. 24).

The authors conclude that horticulture used as a purposeful activity in a group setting had a positive effect on self esteem, well being and hence the quality of life of the participants. Concepts derived from the overall themes included novelty, challenge, learning, sharing, choice and control and these, the authors suggest, could also enhance quality of life when incorporated in group activities other than horticulture.

In the UK, Seller, Fieldhouse and Phelan (1999) reported a pilot study of an allotment-based group called *Fertile Imaginations* for people with mental health problems. The patients were assessed by questionnaire. When asked how the group had helped them in their lives the service users reported four main areas:

- Communication with others
- Learning practical skills/teamwork/planning
- Self-confidence
- Helps concentration

These responses again appear to show the importance of social interaction and group dynamics in a mental health horticulture project. The project may have also helped some members of the group with employment and education as the authors report that two of the participants had entered open employment, one had joined a supported work scheme and one had started attending adult education classes. In a detailed examination of the meaning of the group to nine of its members Fieldhouse (2003, *in press*) reported that they experienced it as a restorative environment which promoted self-awareness. The meaningful work of cultivating the allotment fostered the building of the social network which was so valuable to the group:

> "The group is a social network constructed exclusively by the network members' use of it and is particularly valued for being self-generated in this way. Participants' belief in the group's supportiveness relates to it being an *occupational* group in that individuals' commitment is regularly demonstrated through collective activity. Each participant regards the others as having something positive to contribute and, more significantly, each person experiences the others experiencing them in a similar positive way" (Fieldhouse, 2003, *in press*).

One group of patients which may be at particular risk of social isolation is that suffering from intractable epilepsy. These patients frequently have limited

---

[5] *Semi-structured interviews do not have a fixed set of questions like a questionnaire but a list of themes and questions to be covered.*
Relevant themes can be identified and followed.

opportunity for social contact and may benefit from the group dynamics associated with horticultural therapy programmes. Bennett, So and Smith (1999) reported that following participation in a horticultural therapy programme members reported an increase in social activities in the community and felt more involved in the activities. All participants reported that they had enjoyed the experience of being with others in the programme.

Gardens for patients with dementia

Another specific area of mental health in which therapeutic horticulture has found a place is the care and treatment of patients suffering from Alzheimer's disease and other forms of dementia. Gardens have been designed that provide a safe and stimulating environment for patients and sensory stimuli associated with gardens and gardening have been used to provoke memories in reminiscence therapy.

Hoover (1994) discusses the appropriateness of the design of the garden to the level of deterioration of the patient and the degree of stimulation required. He also discusses remembrance therapy in the context of archetypal landscapes, a concept developed by Messervy (1990; quoted in Hoover, 1994) and suggests that these landscapes refer to themes of human emotion and development. The six landscapes and their associated themes are:

water – *purity*; mountains and rock – *safety and strength*; islands – *contemplation and the feeling of peacefulness*; promenades – *command and power, feeling in control*; caves – *exploration and excitement*; sky – *inspiration, the feeling of being uplifted.*

The relationship between these elements of landscape and their emotional themes can be used to design gardens which correspond to levels of human emotional development and stages of Alzheimer's disease which mimics such development in reverse.

Beckwith and Gilster (1997) suggest a model for a *'paradise'* garden which has four key elements –

enclosing wall, water, canopy, and *hill.* The enclosing wall is of particular significance because it creates the space of the garden and it is a feature of many gardens designed specifically for patients with Alzheimer's disease:

> "The enclosing wall creates the paradise garden. The term *'paradise'* is a transliteration of the Persian word *Pairidaez: pairi-*, meaning around and *-daeza* meaning wall. These enclosing walls associated with a residence, originally constructed of mud or stone, provided a degree of privacy essential to family life. The walls sheltered plants from the searing wind which swept the desert; they protected against undesirable entry of thief and wild beast; and they secured the space for pleasure of shade, fruit and flower... For the individual with Alzheimer's disease, the walled or fenced space serves as a refuge" (Beckwith and Gilster, 1997, p. 7).

Beckwith and Gilster go on to discuss the role of water, the tree canopy and the hill as sources of stimulation to the patient and as symbols of paradise and refuge. They describe the application of the model to the construction of three gardens at the Alois Alzheimer Center in Cincinnati, Ohio. Each of these three gardens is designed to address the different physical, environmental and social needs of the patient as the disease progresses.

Similarly, Ebel (1991) discusses the provision of matched horticultural activities to the stage of deterioration of the patient. She suggests that:

> "A rehabilitative approach using behavioural strategies and environmental modifications can improve physical and mental functions of people with dementia, often allowing them to perform at their highest ability. Optimal functioning and esteem-building need to become the goals of rehabilitation intervention for patients with early-stage dementia; sensory stimulation, awareness outside of self, and bringing pleasure to the patient should become

the goals of late stage dementia intervention" (Ebel, 1991, p. 4).

Mooney and Nicell (1992) examined the number of violent incidents and falls at five nursing homes for patients with Alzheimer's disease. At nursing homes without gardens there was a rise in the number of incidents in two consecutive years as the condition of the residents deteriorated, whilst at the homes with gardens instances of violence and falls actually fell slightly:

> "In the garden institutions, the rate of violent incidents declined by 19% between 1989 and 1990 while the total rate of incidents fell by 3.5% over the same period. In the non-garden institutions, the rate of violent incidents increased by 681% and the total rate of incidents increased by 319%" (Mooney and Nicell, 1992, p.26).

They also evaluated the garden of one of the homes that was especially designed for patients with Alzheimer's disease. This garden had a 'figure-of-eight' looped path (i.e. no dead-ends - this is a feature of many garden designs for Alzheimer's patients), handrails and a smooth path which produced little glare. They found that all residents were able to use the garden without problem. In one of the other gardens, not especially designed for patients with dementia, only 42% of the residents were observed to move through it without confusion.

They suggest the following design considerations:

- Make the garden a continuous spatial unit with strongly defined boundaries, preferably through which residents cannot see.

- All aspects of micro-climatic comfort should be considered, which means protection from sun and wind and reduction of glare.

- Furniture should be heavy and stable with seat heights of about 18 inches.

- Ideally, the garden should be located at the end of a corridor and the exterior door should allow views and access into the garden. This is because residents tend to walk corridors and 'get stuck' at the end of them, not realizing that they can turn around and walk the other way. Since the tendency is to walk forward, circular or loop corridors and walkways minimize frustration. A garden at the end of a corridor is readily discovered and acts as a loop which returns residents to the building and facilitates walking (Mooney and Nicell, 1992, p.29).

(For a review of issues in designing gardens for patients with Alzheimer's disease see also Lovering, 1990.)

Cohen-Mansfield and Werner (1998) studied the effects of escorted visits to outdoor gardens on patients with dementia who were particularly prone to wandering and pacing. Approximately half of the patients had Alzheimer's disease and the other half had dementia of an unknown aetiology. After a 10 day baseline period patients were escorted to the gardens for two half-hour visits per day for 20 days. Detailed observations of the patients were made throughout the study both by researchers and by the nursing staff. A statistically significant reduction in trespassing behaviour (entering other patient's rooms or nurses' area) and a measurable but non-significant reduction in pacing were observed. In terms of mood, the patients showed significantly more pleasure and interest during the garden visit phase of the study compared with the baseline measurements. There was also a decline in anxiety but no change in depression or anger.

The authors noted a number of minor difficulties during the study - the attachment of patients to the researchers; the effect of the weather on visits and the occasional reluctance of patients to go outside. However, they conclude:

> "This study supports the use of outdoor visits for improving the well-being of nursing home residents who tend to pace and for decreasing disruptive behaviors such as trespassing. A closer examination of the process reveals

variability among the residents in their response to the outdoor visits, as well as practical limitations for a continuous practice of the intervention. Whereas future studies need to investigate the inter-participant differences in responsiveness, innovative architectural and environmental designs are needed to make this intervention truly viable" (Cohen-Mansfield and Werner, 1998, pp. 434-435).

Mather, Nemecek and Oliver (1997) evaluated the effect of access to a garden on the behaviour of patients with Alzheimer's disease at a special care unit. They measured the levels of disruptive behaviour and found no statistically significant reduction in the total level during the summer period, when garden use was at its highest, compared to the rest of the year. However, they noted that use of the garden was generally low. Those patients who used the garden more often exhibited less disruptive behaviour and less sleep disturbance than the average, although these differences were not statistically significant. This lack of significance is attributed to the small sample in the study.

It is also possible that regular participation in gardening may offer some protection against the development of dementia. In a prospective study of over 2000 older people living in the Gironde area of France, Fabrigoule et al (1995) showed that those who gardened, travelled or carried out odd jobs or knitting were significantly less likely to develop dementia than those who did not:

"Even after adjustment for age, baseline cognitive performance, physical capability, and occupational activities, the risk of dementia for older subjects who travel, do odd jobs, knit or garden was about half that of subjects who did not participate in these activities. These results seem to confirm the possible protective effect of an active life style on cognitive function in older people" (Fabrigoule et al, 1995, pp. 488-489).

The mechanism for this apparent protective effect is not clear but the authors suggest that these essentially complex activities may stimulate cognitive functions and thereby protect them. Reading, watching television, playing parlour games, associating with others, child care and visiting friends or family did not lower the risk of developing dementia.

Therapeutic horticulture for children with mental health problems

Horticulture has also been used to help children with mental health problems.

McGinnis (1989) described a gardening program for in-patients at a children's psychiatric unit. Gardening activities were combined with discussion groups, and horticulture and observations of the garden were used to stimulate discussion. For example:

"The death of a cauliflower plant afforded the opportunity to talk about grief. The children verbalized feelings surrounding the death of pets, grandparents and other relatives. Discussion was easily steered to the subject of abandonment, a topic of greater significance to many of these patients. The group chose to bury their dead cauliflower in the garden" (McGinnis, 1989, p. 89).

McGinnis concludes that the project was successful and helped the patients to experience self-fulfilment, learn basic biology and develop group activities:

"Through participation in this project, the patients experienced the pride of accomplishment, practiced teamwork, coped successfully with a long delay in gratification for their efforts and learned certain basic principles of botany and reproductive biology. They discussed feelings of fear, sadness, abandonment and pride, as well as family issues. Certain elements of the gardening program allowed staff to assess their patients' motor skills, provide an acceptable outlet for their patients' aggression and gain new insight into their patients' problems and personalities"

(McGinnis, 1989, p. 91).

Horticulture and garden projects associated with residential special schools in the UK have been described by Reeves (1998), Rookes (1998) and Nixon and Read (1998).

Nixon and Read cited detailed case examples of two boys suffering from complex behavioural and mental health problems classed as Pervasive Development Disorder (one diagnosed as having 'Multiple Complex Developmental Disorder' and the other 'High Functioning Autism'). Specific interventions involving garden activities were designed for each of the boys. These took into consideration the specific needs of each child and their individual goals. For example the intervention for one of the boys was structured under the following specific categories:

- Promote general learning
- Creating Structure/Routine
- Creating Meaning
- Creating a Sense of Self
- Providing Visual Cues (Visually Supported Learning)
- Simplifying Instructions
- Giving Control (Actual and Perceived) and Increasing Participation

The authors observe that although it is difficult to quantify improvement and progress the interventions appear to have been successful for both boys:

"It is notoriously difficult to accurately quantify and qualify progress and maybe even to define what constitutes success. Perhaps the simplest indicator of the success of horticulture at the school is the sustained enthusiasm and co-operation of the young people, such as Martin both in absolute and relative terms" (Nixon and Read, 1998, p. 74).

A more formal measure of the success of the programme was provided by analysis of the record sheets and progress reports for the boys:

"It is thus possible to determine that Leo's

average mark during Horticulture has risen from 56% during the first term to 82% for the last full term, and that his general average has risen from 24% before starting the personalized programme. Serious incidents in which he has been involved have declined from 73 per year to 6. Within horticultural sessions concentration and attention span have risen from 32% to 62.5% average in 2 years" (Nixon and Read, 1998, p. 75).

Although most studies focus on the benefits of therapeutic horticulture to patients, Smith (1998) discusses the role that a horticultural therapy programme can have in enabling student psychiatric nurses to gain a greater understanding of patients' problems. She concludes that:

"HT, both for patients and students, provides an opportunity to use group process and gardening activities to foster a sense of therapeutic community on the inpatient mental health wards. It allowed students to assess client functioning in a group setting, conduct a group experience from start to finish and assist persons with mental illness in both the therapeutic alliance as well as in pleasurable activities that relate to an appreciation of beauty" (Smith, 1998, p. 20).

Other studies involving horticulture and mental health which showed similar benefits to those studies already described are listed in Table 1 (see page 20).

The use of horticulture for people with learning disabilities

Many of the activities associated with horticulture and gardening are not complex and can be learned and carried out by people with learning disabilities both for the development of practical and social skills and also with a view to possible future employment (the status of work as a function and goal of therapeutic horticulture in relation to people with learning disabilities is discussed later).

Cowden (1969) gives a brief description of an ad hoc work program set up for 19 patients with learning disabilities. A shortage of workers on the local tomato harvest led to a small group of the patients being selected for a short period (20, four hour days) of paid employment. The productivity of the patients was lower than that of the workers but they were better at selecting usable fruit and all of the fruit picked by the patients passed selection. The activity led to an improvement of the patients' colour discrimination and co-ordination. The act of earning money created a feeling of accomplishment and increased self-esteem. They were able to demonstrate promptness in meeting their bus and "good work habits when they cleaned their bus each evening".

Smith and Aldous (1994) used the Tennessee Self Concept Scale (TSCS), a questionnaire-based assessment, to measure the improvement in self-esteem and general well-being of 11 students with learning difficulties and found a statistically significant increase in scores of self-concept after four months of participation in the programme. The authors note that:

> "The improved score suggests that participation in horticultural pursuits increased the students feeling of value and worth in that they considered themselves more desirable than before as individuals. Therapeutic horticulture provided each individual with the opportunity to express themselves in a positive way, thus influencing their self-esteem in a positive way" (Smith and Aldous, 1994, p. 217).

Sarver (1985) gives a personal evaluation of a pilot programme of elementary school gardening on emotional well-being in a group of 'learning disabled' students aged 8-12. The students gained satisfaction from seeing that they could succeed at something - growing flowers and vegetables, they also learned that success was related to "careful execution of well-devised plans". The gardening programme also provided social benefits:

> "With plants as learning partners the students came to value themselves in new ways. As their plants changed each day, they saw the results of their hard work. Frustration and failure gave way to productivity and success. Indeed, agritherapy is really a form of success therapy. Other benefits of this approach include: acceptance of diversity in nature and people; appreciation of beauty in the environment; social development through cooperative effort; and a willingness to accept the importance of order and structure. All of these values will help my students as they move along the arduous journey they face. In perhaps no small way, agritherapy may prove to have been a positive and timely intervention for many of them" (Sarver, 1985, p. 396).

Some additional studies involving the use of horticulture for children and adults with learning difficulties and behavioural problems are listed in Table 2 (see page 21).

Gardening and older people

There is an extensive literature dealing with the design of tools, techniques and gardens for older people (and also those with physical disabilities) and Thrive is able to provide much practical information and advice. The focus of this literature review, however, is on the benefits derived from the process of gardening and in that area the literature is considerably smaller. Indeed, in a recent UK report on *Gardening in Later Life* (2002) Bhatti concludes that:

> "Gardening in later life has not been systematically and extensively researched in the UK, and there are significant gaps in our knowledge. Questions remain as to precisely how much the garden is valued, what kinds of problems it poses, and what kinds of benefits supported gardening can bring to elderly people" (Bhatti, 2002, p. 16).

The report was primarily concerned with gardening activities in the home garden and not on therapeutic aspects of horticulture.

The link between physical activity and health in older people has been extensively researched and there is a mass of evidence which suggests that physical activity is associated with good health and reduced risk factors for heart disease and other illnesses (for example see: Seeman and Chen, 2002; Burke et al, 2001; for a review see: DiPetro, 2001). In a major study of physical activity and risk factors for coronary heart disease in a large group of elderly Dutch men (the Zutphen Study) Caspersen et al (1991) found a statistically significant reduction in risk factors in those men that still gardened compared with those that were less active. Surprisingly cycling was not associated with a lower level of risk but perhaps this was related to the relatively easy cycling conditions found in the country.

The association of gardening with cognitive well-being has also been suggested. Fabrigoule's study of over 2,000 older people in France (Fabrigoule et al, 1995) showed that those who gardened, travelled or carried out odd jobs or knitting were significantly less likely to develop dementia than those who did not.

Although gardening has been mentioned as one of the physical activities engaged in by older people, there have been few studies which have looked specifically at the benefits, both physical and psychological, of gardening itself.

In a controlled study Mooney and Milstein (1994) assessed the effects of a horticultural therapy programme on a group of older people in nursing homes in Canada. Forty older people received two sessions of horticultural therapy per week for six months whilst a control group received a plant each for their room and were given a single instruction session in its care. A target ratio of one therapist or volunteer to two residents was maintained where possible, and the therapist worked with the same patients throughout the study, again where possible.

All of the residents were assessed by questionnaire to study their psychological function and focus groups were held with staff and volunteers on the programme to ascertain their perceptions of the effects of the horticultural programme.

The questionnaires used were the Physical and Mental Impairment of Function Evaluation (PAMIE, Gurel et al, 1979), the Multi-focus Assessment Scale for the Frail Elderly (MAS, Coval et al, 1985) and an adaptation of Social Participation and Social Interaction Scales developed by Bradburn and Caplovitz (1965) and Phillips (1967).

Mooney and Milstein (1994) tested for overall deterioration, belligerence/irritability, paranoid/suspicious score, anxiety/depression score and sensory-motor impairment. Although many of the variables did not show a statistically significant change there was a visible trend of improvement in the horticultural therapy group which reversed at the cessation of the programme. The lack of statistical change could, in part, be attributed to the number of residents failing to complete the study (9 in the horticultural therapy group and 8 in the control group). The sub-group which showed the greatest deterioration appeared to benefit the most from horticultural therapy.

Results from the focus group discussions suggested that the horticultural therapy programme had benefits beyond those that could be seen from the results of the questionnaires. The authors note:

> "The therapeutic staff expressed consensus that substantial benefits resulted from the horticulture as therapy program, both within program sessions and carrying over into other aspects of daily life. Among the benefits seen in both facilities were, increased orientation to place, task and seasons, increased attention span, improved or increased interactions with other residents both during and outside of program times, reminiscence, increased or improved physical functioning, displays of initiative, increased motivation, and the

opportunity to experience success and accomplishment" (Mooney and Milstein, 1994, p. 181).

Heliker, Chadwick and O'Connell (2000) used questionnaires and semi-structured interviews to examine the perceived well-being of two groups of older people before and after engaging in a four month gardening program. They found a significant increase in perceived *psychological* well-being of both groups and a significant improvement in the *general* well-being of one of the groups. This group had a higher average age than the other, lower annual income and was predominantly African-American. The other group was predominantly Caucasian.

There was no significant difference in the perceived *physical* well-being of either group.

In the interviews the participants were asked questions which evoked a story of the meaning of gardening in their lives. The themes that evoked the most stories were gardening as spiritual healing and therapy, successful gardening experiences, the legacy of gardening (i.e. how they learned to garden) and remembering a favourite childhood tree. The beneficial effects of gardening experienced by the participants were set in the context of 'the personal meaning framework' postulated by Reker and Wong (1988). Gardening had a particular significance and meaning to the participants and they recalled gardening stories with fondness. For some this special meaning was spiritual. They likened gardening to a prayer and spoke of it as a way of relating to God. This spiritual theme did not appear to be associated with any level of education, socio-economic status, culture or background. The interviews appeared to be particularly valuable in eliciting the personal benefits obtained by participating in the gardening programme:

> "The open-ended interview with its opportunity for story sharing and historical elements, free of cultural bias, was most helpful in ascertaining the critical significance and meaning of

gardening for older adults. Qualitative study designs and evaluation of the unique relationship between person and nature might be more appropriate than quantitative methodologies. Remembered gardens and perceived experiences of this garden project were unique in the therapeutic effects to each individual" (Heliker, Chadwick and O'Connell, 2000, p. 53).

The authors also examined the costs of the gardening programme and conclude that at around $1,000 dollars ($1,0360 and $819) for each four month project they appeared to be a cost-effective form of therapy.

Therapeutic horticulture, community gardens and allotments

Many of the therapeutic horticulture projects described so far have been run and managed for the benefit of the local community and some are set in community gardens. A conference held in Nottingham, UK, in 2000 entitled *People, Land and Sustainability – a global view of community gardening* had 'Community Gardening and Health' as one of its themes (see Ferris *et al*, 2001). Other themes such as 'Food Security' were also linked to health and well-being. However, there is, in many cases a clear sense of identity of participants and practitioners with their respective activities. In the US the American Community Gardening Association is well established, having been founded in 1979, and in the UK the Federation of City Farms and Community Gardens is equally active. Similarly, the American Horticultural Therapy Association, and Thrive in the UK, support the interests of practitioners of therapeutic horticulture and horticultural therapy. Perhaps the divergence of therapeutic horticulture and community gardening is manifested by the therapeutic goal of the former and the environmental stance of the latter. However, they are united within the theme of well-being for both the community and the individual; and research carried out on community gardening projects gives evidence to support the therapeutic role of horticulture and gardening.

In the UK, allotments and allotment gardening occupy a unique place in its environment, history and culture (see Crouch and Ward, 1997). The allotment movement is linked with community gardening and therapeutic horticulture and many of the UK projects described in this review are based on allotment sites. Again, many of those participating in allotment gardening, either for their own well-being or for the well-being of others, would classify themselves as 'allotment gardeners' or 'plotholders' rather than 'therapeutic gardeners'. The value of allotment gardening was recognised by a Government committee enquiry (HOC, 1998) which voiced concern at the decline in the number of allotment plots. As a result of this a *Good Practice Guide for the Management of Allotments* was commissioned and published (Crouch, Sempik and Wiltshire, 2001). This lists numerous examples of projects which have been set up to improve the health and well-being of disadvantaged communities and individuals although few, if any, of these projects have been studied in detail.

In the US, community gardens were introduced by European immigrants in the late nineteenth and early twentieth centuries and in many respects they have occupied a similar position and function to allotments in the UK. They have provided food for those on limited incomes, especially during periods of national hardships such as the Panic of 1893 and the Depression of the 1930s (see Bassett, 1981). At the present time they continue to supplement income but they also provide much needed green space, opportunities for social interaction and a setting where quality-of-life issues such as the building of self-esteem can be tackled. However, despite the popularity of community gardens and the activity of the ACGA, research on the benefits of community gardening is still limited although some work has been carried out.

Armstrong (2000) conducted a survey of 20 community garden programmes, maintaining a total of 63 individual gardens, in upstate New York in order to identify the reasons for participation and the benefits derived from them. She found that the most commonly expressed reasons were access to fresh and better tasting foods, enjoyment of nature and the benefit to health, including mental health. She also found that community gardens provided an opportunity for neighbourhood issues to be addressed, this was especially true in low income neighbourhoods.

In their nationwide survey of community gardeners, Waliczek, Mattson and Zajicek (1996) found that gardening produced benefits in the perceived quality of life. Their questionnaire was based around Abraham Maslow's model of the hierarchy of human needs (see Maslow, 1943, 1954) which postulates that people seek to satisfy needs in an order starting with basic physiological needs such as hunger and thirst, then needs of safety and security, and progress to the fulfilment of higher social and psychological needs such as esteem and self-actualisation. Waliczek *et al* (1996) found that gardening appeared to fulfil quality-of-life needs on the higher levels of Maslow's hierarchy i.e. those of esteem and self-actualisation.

Community gardens and minority ethnic communities

Armstrong (2000) found that participation in community gardening programmes in New York by ethnic minorities was high. Overall, approximately 30% of the gardens were cultivated predominantly by African Americans or other racial minorities, and in low income areas this figure was considerably greater.

The importance of community garden spaces called 'casitas' to Puerto Rican inhabitants of the city was studied by Winterbottom (1998), who described them as "an aesthetic, social and spiritual oasis" which "create a social force, fostering memories and building meaningful connections for a displaced community". They are used for social gatherings, religious celebrations, healing, and learning principles of cultivation and medicinal use of plants. When asked why they spent time in the casita the majority of users of the garden responded that they wished to spend time with family and friends, and when asked what they actually did at the casita 70% responded that gardening was their primary activity. The process of gardening and watching the plants grow was important, and for some also therapeutic:

> "Thirty percent responded that the garden made them less nervous, happier, and was 'therapeutic'. Surrounded by a high stress environment and with a lack of accessible natural places, the importance of the garden as a stress reducer appears to be important" (Winterbottom, 1998, p. 91).

Results from the survey of Waliczek *et al* (1996), described in the previous section, showed that African-American and Hispanic gardeners consistently scored the benefits of gardening at a higher level than did Asian or Caucasian gardeners. This led the authors to conclude that for them gardening was of particular importance:

> "To African-American and Hispanic gardeners, some of which may lack economic means of securing land or home ownership, the garden provides extremely important quality-of-life benefits" (Waliczek *et al*, 1996, p. 209).

Table 1 Additional Studies on horticulture and mental health		
Authors	**Client Group**	**Brief Summary of Research**
Talbott, Stern, Ross & Gillen, 1976	Psychiatric patients, mostly with schizophrenia	Following the introduction of flowers into the dining room of a psychiatric hospital there was a statistically significant increase in the time spent in the dining room, vocalization (speech to one another) and food consumed.
Kaiser, 1976	Children with a range of difficulties – autism, learning disabilities, Down's syndrome and schizophrenia	The benefits of the programme were assessed by questionnaire administered to teachers and parents and by interviews with the children. Benefits included: sense of self-esteem, increased awareness and responsibility, practical knowledge, communication, and understanding of concept of work and work experience.
Spelfogel & Modrzakowski, 1980	Psychiatric patients	Brief case study of 2 patients displaying, among other psychiatric symptoms, obsessive behaviours towards perfectionism. The authors suggest that working with plants in a relaxed atmosphere may have helped the patients to overcome this aspect of their illness.
Lloyd, 1986	Long term psychiatric patients	Description of a workscheme (which includes a horticultural workshop) as a source of work-associated benefits for long term patients – satisfaction, self-esteem, sense of identity, social status and a small financial reward.
Williams, 1989	Short term psychiatric in-patients	Encouragement of the assumption of responsibility (for care of plants) and development of 'pride, satisfaction and sense of accomplishment' together with social interaction and co-operative activities.
Goodban & Goodban, 1990a; 1990b	Psychiatric patients	Description of the introduction of a horticultural therapy programme and detailed description of activities (Part 1); two case studies are given in Part 2.

	Table 1 continued...	
Authors	**Client Group**	**Brief Summary of Research**
Bryant, 1991	Confused elderly in-patients (including some with Alzheimer's)	Use of gardening to promote 'sensory integration' - enhancement of sensory and emotional experiences in under stimulated patients.
Vaccaro, Cousino & Vatcher, 1992	Psychiatric patients (mostly outpatients)	Development of work and social skills in a therapeutic horticulture setting for future employment.
Matsuo, Fujiki & Fujiwara, 1997 (Japanese paper with English summary)	Survey of psychiatric hospitals and welfare institutions in Japan	Identification of number of hospitals and institutions using horticulture for therapy or training and the satisfaction levels of patients.
Cohen Mansfield & Werner, 1999	Nursing home residents with dementia, including Alzheimer's disease	Nationwide, US, survey of characteristics and use of outdoor areas for residents.

Table 2 Additional studies on horticulture and learning disabilities and behavioural problems		
Authors	**Client Group**	**Brief Summary of Research**
Airhart, Willis, & Westrick, 1987	Students with learning disabilities	Description of horticulture programme in a greenhouse setting leading to development of work and social skills.
Doxon, Mattson & Jurish, 1987	Adults with learning disabilities	Reduced stress (as measured by lower heart rate, systolic and diastolic blood pressure and electrodermal skin response) was seen in a group of adults with learning disabilities when they were working in a greenhouse compared with when they were at a training centre.

Table 2 continued...

Authors	Client Group	Brief Summary of Research
Hoffman & Castro-Blanco, 1988	Mixed class of children with different learning abilities	Integration of gifted and learning disabled children into science classes and 'hands-on' horticultural activities.
Dout, Airhart & Willis, 1989	Long term psychiatric patients	Description of a workscheme (which includes a horticultural workshop) as a source of work-associated benefits for long term patients - satisfaction, self-esteem, sense of identity, social status and a small financial reward.
Kay, 1990	Adults with Autism	Description of a rural farm community 'Bittersweet Farms', for autistic adults in Ohio. Development of basic and work skills, leisure skills and community integration.
Giddan and Giddan, 1991, (eds)	Adults with Autism	Edited collection of papers on 'Bittersweet Farms' and associated issues connected with autism.
Schleien et al, 1991	Adults with Autism	Development of horticultural skills for leisure and possible employment.
Eddy & Sadof, 1993	Adults with learning disabilities and mental health problems	Training in specific skills for identifying and assessing numbers of pests in a greenhouse 'Integrated Pest Management' (IPM) programme. Two individuals were retained as IPM 'scouts' in a sheltered work environment and experience with these suggests that such relatively skilled work could be carried out by others with disabilities under the Americans with Disabilities Act (1990).

3 Horticulture, nature, aggression and peace

There is evidence in the literature that the landscape environment can have a beneficial effect both when experienced passively and also when engaged with actively through horticulture and gardening. Research carried out on experiences in wilderness areas suggests that these can have a profound psychological effect leading to feelings of peace, tranquillity and sometimes deeper, spiritual expression. Such effects of nature have been harnessed in more controlled environments, such as prison gardens in order to modify offending or antisocial behaviour. Horticultural work, apart from providing its own intrinsic benefits, has also enabled skills to be learned which can be used to obtain employment. All of these effects help to promote self-esteem and well-being.

The 'wilderness experience'

Recently specific 'wilderness therapy' programmes have been developed in the US. These have their origins in Outward Bound programmes introduced in the 1960s which are standardised programmes of activities including climbing, hiking and camping in a wilderness setting, but without specific counselling or therapy (see Russell, 2001). Many of the new wilderness therapy programmes, however, include counselling or group discussions focused on the problems or illnesses of the participants.

Although the concept of horticulture and cultivation may seem very far removed from that of wilderness the underlying themes of nature and interaction with nature are common. The literature in this area may add further evidence for the beneficial effects of gardening and horticulture and it is therefore useful to consider briefly some aspects of the 'wilderness experience'. The work of psychologists, Rachel and Stephen Kaplan on restorative environments (see later), has its foundations in wilderness research

(see Kaplan and Talbot, 1983; Kaplan and Kaplan, 1989). They have examined studies carried out on participants in wilderness programmes, and have been involved in their own wilderness research for many years. They suggest that the most important and most valued element is the enjoyment of nature and its beauty. The use of specialist skills and the confrontation of hazards and hardships are of much lesser importance. The implication for horticulture and gardening is important to the extent that appreciation of nature and the nature experience do not necessarily have to take place in a harsh and challenging environment and much of the research carried out in a wilderness setting may also be applicable to a garden or allotment.

Kaplan and Talbot (1983) note the sense of self-esteem and insight that develop from wilderness experience and the awareness of self relative to the vastness and timelessness of nature. They suggest that the elements of the experience could be grouped as follows:

- *Tranquillity, peace, silence*
- *Integration, wholeness*
- *Oneness - the sense of being at one with the universe.*

Similar themes have been described in relation to gardening and horticulture experiences and are present throughout this literature review.

Davis-Berman and Berman (1989) carried out a detailed evaluation of the 'Wilderness Therapy Program' for adolescents with psychiatric and behavioural problems. This particular programme comprises trips in the wilderness with counselling, and has specified treatment goals. They found that measures of self-esteem, self-efficacy and behavioural symptoms were significantly improved by the programme.

Powch (1994) discusses the experiences and perceptions of women (some of whom were victims of sexual abuse) who have participated in wilderness therapy and also those of the therapists themselves. She suggests that in addition to enhancing self-esteem and a sense of control in women wilderness therapy invokes a long-lost sense of spirituality. Fredrickson and Anderson (1999) also observed a spiritual dimension in the experiences of two groups of women backpacking and canoeing in wilderness areas.

Williams (2000) reviewed the literature on wilderness therapy for adolescents with behavioural and delinquency problems and compared the reported outcomes with those of conventional treatment. He found that wilderness therapy appeared to be more effective than conventional therapy for that particular client group.

Hyer *et al* (1996) examined the effects of Outward Bound programmes on a group of US war veterans suffering from combat-related post-traumatic stress disorder (PTSD). Although they found no discernable effects on objective measures of the symptoms of their patients they reported that from a subjective point of view many patients found the experience valuable in building self-esteem and self-confidence. The researchers themselves, some of whom participated in the Outward Bound programme noted that it appeared to have been a profound experience and that "it does not seem possible that such events, experiences, and outcome were of little or no significance". They suggest further research on such programmes particularly on patients with less severe disorder who appeared to respond better to the programme. They add that the methodology currently used to study PTSD may not be able to detect the full benefits of the Outward Bound programmes and may need to be revised not only to make it sensitive to those programmes but also to better reflect the effects of standard treatment. It is highly likely that the effects of many 'outdoor' therapies, including the Outward Bound Experience, wilderness therapy and also gardening and horticulture are subtle and may not easily be detected and separated from the effects of other influences. There is a clear need for the development of new measuring instruments for studying such therapies.

Landscape view and aggression

In a recent study Kuo and Sullivan (2001) showed that residents living in US apartments with nearby trees exhibited significantly less aggression against their partners than those living in apartments in barren surroundings. This effect was independent of levels of stress, mood or social integration and therefore appeared to be mediated by the effect of the environment alone. Those living in apartments with nearby trees had a significantly higher directed attention than those with barren surroundings. They also found that the level of aggression was inversely correlated with the measure of attentional functioning; i.e. residents with the greatest levels of aggression had the least capacity for directed attention. This suggests that those respondents in barren surroundings were experiencing a level of mental fatigue whilst those with nearby trees experienced a restorative effect. Attention restoration theory and the restorative effect of nature are discussed later.

Landscape view and sickness in prison

Moore (1981) examined the sickness presentation of inmates of the State Prison of Michigan and its relationship to the design of the prison. He found that the location of a prisoner in the cell block, gallery level or the side of the prison in which he was confined significantly influenced his probability of reporting sick. Although the major influence in precipitating sickness appeared to be the lack of privacy associated with some locations within the prison the view of open farm land afforded from some of the cell windows appeared to be protective:

> "Surprisingly, a statistically significant greater chance of coming to sick call was observed among those prisoners living in the 'inside' half of cell blocks 1,2,3,4, and 5 than among those on the 'outside half'....

> The 'inside' refers to that half of each cell block which has cells closest to the prison yard side of the cell block. The 'outside' half faces toward the 'free world' side of the prison wall. Since this was an unexpected finding, the possible interaction of gallery level, side of block and race was tested.

> The predicted odds of *not* coming to sick call are greater for prisoners who live in cells located on the 'outside' half of the cell blocks 1,2,3,4, and 5. There is something about the 'inside' half which is influencing prisoner decisions to attend sick call.

> With each half of each cell block being essentially symmetrical, there appears (to be) no specific design feature which would be suspect as causal.

> A more subtle factor may exist in the differences between 'inside' and 'outside' halves. When windows of the cell blocks are opened so prisoners may look out of the cell block, those on the 'inside' half look into the prison yard. Those on the 'outside' half look out to green farmland and forests which are considered preferred environments. This type of view may provide some stress reduction in itself" (Moore, 1981, p. 32).

Although the complaints that the prisoners presented with vary greatly (e.g. gastrointestinal, respiratory, orthopaedic, skin etc.) they may all represent a desire for attention, nurturing and psychological support and care.

Therapeutic horticulture and offenders

Rice and Remy (1994a, 1998) carried out a study of the San Francisco Garden Project which was started in 1984 by Cathrine Sneed (an African American environmental justice activist). They describe in detail the psychological, environmental and social factors relating to a sample of the prison population and the effect of a horticultural programme on them. The background of the selected sample is given by the authors in a previous publication (Rice and Remy, 1994b). Forty eight inmates, matched for race and gender, were randomly assigned to horticultural projects or to other projects.

The horticulture group took part in discussions on organic gardening and were taught organic gardening methods. Food and flowers grown by the project were donated to San Francisco's homeless shelters and to a programme providing meals to house-bound AIDS patients.

Baseline data was obtained and the subjects were interviewed again on their discharge and 3 months later. Information regarding their family background and drug history was taken and they completed a questionnaire for the assessment of psychosocial functioning which examined their level of depression, hostility, risk-taking and desire for help (in seeking to end substance abuse).

The background data for the inmates showed a large proportion of inmates without intact families during childhood and adolescence, history of neglect, physical and sexual abuse, experience of violence between their parents and use of illegal drugs.

Subjects who reported detachment from their mothers (by statements such as "mother didn't love me, spend time with me" or (didn't) "teach me about drugs" in their interviews) showed evidence of depression in their baseline interviews as compared with those subjects who had reported maternal attachment. This depression score was reduced in those subjects who participated in the Garden Project and this reduction was maintained at follow up.

Hostility scores of the subjects were related to a number of different factors but childhood injury appears to have been a major influence which the authors suggest is "the engine behind subject hostility at baseline" (Rice and Remy, 1998, p. 182).

The effectiveness of the Garden Project on hostility appeared to be dependent on childhood injury and also on the ethnic origin of the subjects:

> "Subjects who had never been injured in childhood had lower hostility scores and there was no change over time for those subjects. All the change was in those who had been injured...Injured White subjects in the garden became significantly less hostile by discharge and returned to baseline levels at follow-up. Injured African Americans in the garden were slightly more hostile at discharge and significantly less hostile at follow-up, particularly in comparison to African Americans in the control group" (Rice and Remy, 1998, p. 182).

The garden group also maintained their desire for help in combating drug use:

> "Horticultural therapy treatment retained at follow-up included lower depression in subjects who had emotionally attached mother, reduced number of substances used and a desire for help" (Rice and Remy, 1998, p. 185).

The differences between the effects of participating in the Garden Project on White subjects and African Americans may have been related to the different childhood histories of the two groups.

Another prison gardening project that has been described was developed by The New Jersey Department of Corrections and Division of Juvenile Services in conjunction with Rutgers University - Cook College (Flagler, 1993, 1994, 1995). This project was directed at young offenders in the 15 - 18 age group and had specific aims and objectives in teaching horticultural and other skills to trainees, and enabling them to understand the role of these specific skills as life skills:

> "One goal of this specialized training has been to make New Jersey's adjudicated youth more employable. Another goal has been to impart personal development skills that can lead to improved self-esteem and outlook" (Flagler, 1995, p. 185).

The intended benefits of the scheme could be summarised as follows:

- Provide activity – in the form of meaningful work

- Produce quality food – to help improve the quality of life in the institution through a better diet

- Provide learning experience – in work ethic, responsibility, basic social skills, problem solving and decision making. These skills are important for future employment

- Enable success in horticulture – an opportunity to succeed and build self-confidence and self-esteem.

The training programme recognised the success of participants by awarding them a certificate and for many this was the first certificate of achievement that they had ever received. The success of the scheme was evaluated by questionnaires completed by participants.

For 85% the training programme was the first time

that they had entered a college classroom, the same 85% reported an interest in going to college. Eighty percent reported that the course had provided ideas for future careers. Eighty seven percent believed that they could improve the quality of their lives as a result of the programme. This could be as a result of the job skills they acquired; the experience they obtained; the contacts they made; and ideas they had about future training. The majority of participants, therefore, appear to have regarded the horticulture programme as a positive influence for future work, education or training.

One problem that the authors noted early in the programme was the high level of turnover of inmates leading to a lack of continuity and disruption to the project. They attempted to counter this by designing the curriculum so that each lesson stood independently and also by using videotape of lessons to bring new students up to date with past classes.

Finch (1995) described the 'Green Brigade' programme for juvenile offenders in Bexar County, Texas. Youths on the programme received the hourly minimum wage for six hours on a Saturday. Two of the hours were spent under instruction in topics such as plant growth, pruning, propagation, irrigation, xeriscaping (creating a garden that uses less water than a conventional one), horticultural careers, and garden construction. The remaining four hours were allocated for work hours, predominantly on projects in the county parks.

Of 63 participants in the project in 1993-1994, 21 obtained better jobs and two started college courses. The project supervisor credited the project with providing the participants with horticultural knowledge "that improved their work habits", self-esteem, confidence and appreciation of property. The children also gained an understanding of the process of authority by acting as mentors for younger children on a gardening project. The success of the project could be measured by the fact that in 1994 it was classified "as an outstanding project in criminal justice by the Texas Attorney General" (Finch, 1995,

p. 120).

de Montmollin and his colleagues (de Montmollin et al, 1986) evaluated a *sociotherapeutic workshop* (STW) for inmates suffering from severe personality disorders at Champ-Dollon remand prison in Geneva. The STW consisted of a multi purpose workshop, a small gymnasium, a staff room and a garden plot with a greenhouse. They did not separate gardening from other activities at the STW which also included discussion groups, creative work and social skills training. They used a questionnaire to survey both the inmates and prison guards (10 inmates and 11 guards) and also used an additional two dimensional grid scale for the inmates. The majority of prison guards (73%) enjoyed working at the STW and over one third of them perceived that they had better contact with the inmates as a result of the STW.

The inmates reported that the STW produced a number of psychological benefits including better coping with imprisonment, improved communication, improved manual skills, increased self-respect and respect for others and increased control of violent potential. In general, there was agreement in the perception of the benefits of the STW by both inmates and guards. However, only a minority of inmates believed that the STW prepared them for release or diminished their risk of recidivism. The authors conclude that a *sociotherapeutic workshop*, functioning as a therapeutic community, can provide a satisfactory treatment setting for remand prisoners with severe personality disorders. It can improve their well-being, reduce the risk of suicide and lead to better communication skills and increased respect towards others.

McGuin and Relf (2001) studied a group of six juvenile offenders enrolled at an Alternative Education Program Project School in a rural county in Virginia. They examined psychological factors before, and at the end of a 17 week programme which was based on job descriptions provided by horticultural professionals and "designed to present horticulture as a potential and attainable vocation". They assessed social bonding (the youths' bond to society which is an indicator of the likelihood of offending) and their career aspirations using a test based on Hirschi's tests of social bond for juvenile delinquency (see: Hirschi, 1969). They also examined behavioural reports and logs kept on the students by their mentors and interviewed staff on the programme.

The results obtained showed a statistically significant increase in the mean social bond score. Analysis of the daily behavioural reports showed a significant change in the youths' ability to complete tasks - an indicator of social bond. There was also a positive change in attitude to personal success and education as measured by the Career Aspiration Test (see, McGuin and Relf, 2001, pp. 430-431):

> "The results from this test appear to indicate that positive changes in attitudes about potential for personal success and job preparedness occurred for the youths at the AEPPS and were supported by the mentors' log. From the pretest to posttest there appeared to be an overall positive change in the youths' views on education, specifically in the level of education that the participants wanted to finish. According to Hirschi (1969), the greater a youth's attachment to education, the less likely he/she is to commit deviant acts. An adolescent's view of his/her expected level of education hints at how much that youth has internalised the cultural goals of success and aspirations" (McGuin and Relf, 2001, p. 432).

The authors conclude that:

> "This research indicates that this vocational horticulture curriculum may be a tool to improve social bonding of juvenile offenders, and that the tested curriculum appeared to be effective at evoking certain changes in attitudes about personal success and individual perceptions of personal job preparedness. The data appear to indicate that this curriculum has motivated these youths to develop goals and seriously consider their future plans. Another apparent

benefit of this curriculum was that it provided the youths with the chance to develop pride in themselves through work and the opportunity to prove that they could be successful, and hence, develop a positive self image" (McGuin and Relf, 2001, p. 433).

The programme also provided the opportunity for five of the youths to obtain horticultural job placements for their summer vacations.

Therapeutic horticulture and sex offenders

Gibson and Hughes (2000) described a garden project for the treatment of violent sex offenders at Atascaedro State Hospital in California. Initially eight patients were assigned to the project but as it was observed by other patients and staff more interest in gardening was generated and additional groups were created. The patients engaged in four one-hourly training sessions per week but were free to work in the garden during their leisure time.

The authors discuss the benefits of the garden project to the patients in general terms under the headings of *self-esteem, self-efficacy, frustration tolerance, delayed gratification and leisure skills*. Involvement in the garden project may help to develop these attributes.

They report that self-efficacy, "the belief or expectation that one has the ability to perform a task successfully in a given situation" (described by Hall 1989, and quoted by Gibson and Hughes, 2000) counters the general feeling of failure found in the patients. The development of horticultural skills may also provide an opportunity for the patient to engage in gardening, both as a leisure activity and for employment, and so prevent the boredom associated with unfilled free time. Boredom is seen as a "high-risk factor for re-offence".

They conclude that:

"Preliminary patient response to horticultural therapy with repeat sex offenders at Atascadero State Hospital is encouraging. Its overall effect on post-hospital adaptation will need to be evaluated through further research" (Gibson and Hughes, 2000, p. 25).

Therapeutic horticulture and drug misuse in prison

A problem frequently associated with inmates of prisons and correctional institutions is that of drug misuse. Richards and Kafami (1999) describe a therapeutic horticulture programme for prisoners with drug-related problems referred to the Patuxent Institution in Maryland ("Maryland's primary treatment-orientated, co-educational, maximum security correctional facility in Jessup, Maryland"). The programme is run on an annual basis over six months and involves lectures and therapy sessions in addition to horticultural activities. The overall philosophy of the programme involves organic principles of gardening and ecological concepts and is strongly rooted in African culture and principles:

"The program's guiding motto is, "Gardening to be Drug-Free". Offenders learn that the way drugs destroy their bodies is the way that pollution as chemicals destroy plants. Gardening is done chemical-free. The entire program is based on Afro-centric principles and is cosmological in nature, a mixture of cultural, spiritual and universal principles (Jackson, 1997). Offenders first learn about the Gaia Concept. Coming from the word geology, Gaia is the goddess of the Earth, thereby suggesting that the Earth itself is not inanimate - it is a living organism (Jackson, 1996). The next concept introduced is the idea of ecology, not in the traditional environmental sense, but rather as related to echo, feedback, and relationships in which individuals feel a connectiveness to what they see and produce in the gardens (Jackson, 1997). An important concept,

usufruct, teaches the offenders that people should engage in shared, responsible use of the land, as opposed to the concept of ownership. The final concept, FINN, states that roles of animals and plants in the environment, rather than the needs of humans, should be stressed (Jackson, 1997)" (Richards and Kafami, 1999, pp. 185-186)[6].

Richards and Kafami identified two specific categories of factors related to drug abuse which they termed the *Vulnerability to Addiction* (VTA) and the *Resistance to Addiction* (RTA). Factors associated with VTA were psychological symptoms, tension and distress whilst those associated with RTA were a higher sense of self-efficacy, positive expectations and confidence in coping skills. They studied 33 offenders (8 female, 25 male) and found a statistically significant reduction in factors related to VTA but no significant improvement in indicators of RTA. An improvement in the psychological well-being of the subjects was supported by anecdotal statements of the therapists engaged in the programme.

The differential effect of horticulture on these two groups of factors may have been due to different sensitivities of the tests used; tests for VTA factors were possibly more sophisticated and had greater sensitivities. It is also possible that the horticultural programme had less effect on RTA due to the inherent nature of the sample of inmates studied:

"Offenders are often viewed as self-defeating, have limited insight in how their problems are caused by their own behavior, and have marked deficits in the self-monitoring and self-regulatory processes that anchor behavior. These pervasive personality and cognitive deficits overlap conceptually with RTA. Although HT may quickly reduce reactive psychological symptoms related to substance abuse such as those the CRAVE [tests for indicators of VTA: reviewer's note] is intended to measure, HT may have less of an effect on increasing the positive resources that are already lacking in offenders.

These deficits and defects may impose a ceiling on gains in RTA that can be achieved in a short-term programme" (Richards and Kafami, 1999, pp. 190-191).

Therapeutic horticulture, therefore, produced a significant benefit in some psychological aspects related to drug use but failed to affect others. Those factors not affected by the programme may be intrinsically more difficult to alter, or require a longer programme or some additional form of therapy.

Rice, Remy and Whittlesey (1998) briefly review the use of horticulture in the rehabilitation of offenders with drug problems and provide short case studies of four prison horticulture projects in the US for substance misusers.

Therapeutic horticulture in the treatment of substance and alcohol misuse

Therapeutic horticulture has been used in the treatment of substance and alcohol misuse outside the prison environment. Neuberger (1995) describes the case study of a 30 year old man who had been a 'glue sniffer' for 14 years. He was enrolled on a therapeutic horticulture programme at Langenfeld Psychiatric Hospital near Cologne in Germany where 27% of the participants were drug or alcohol misusers. Prior to enrolment in the programme the man's sole interest and motivation had appeared to be sniffing glue yet after only 3 months on the programme his interests had broadened and he had a girlfriend for the first time in 12 years. Two years later he was in employment in a fruit and vegetable business and had not returned to substance misuse. Neuberger suggests that there are three facets of the therapy which contribute to improvement – *improvement of the self image, improvement of*

awareness and contact and activation of resources.

"Garden work gave daily structure, and he was occupied meaningfully. Reasons for his continuity may lie in the experience of a meaningful daily routine; the amazement about what came out of the soil; and that he had found someone he could cooperate with, a person whom he had chosen. He used more and more the communicative opportunities provided, especially when he was digging potatoes" (Neuberger, 1995, p. 244).

Communication and group work, therefore, appeared to be important in the recovery process.

Horticultural therapy has also been used as an associated therapy in the treatment of alcoholism. Cornille *et al* (1987) described a project at the Florida Alcoholism Treatment Center where horticulture is used in addition to other forms of therapy. Patients receive formal therapy sessions and are also assigned to groups with responsibilities for specific areas of the hospital grounds which they manage and improve. The programme leads to the development of group identities and personal and group development. Although the authors did not give detailed benefits resulting from the horticultural activities they discuss these in relation to six levels of experience which they considered to be of importance in such a programme. These were: *body awareness, body effectiveness, impact of action on environment, impact of action on self and others, impact of thinking, and creativity*. The programme works as a therapeutic community and benefits to the patient derive, in part, from the membership of a group engaged in a worthwhile activity:

"At each of these experience levels, the recovering addict has the opportunity to move

---

⁶ References to 'Jackson' relate to unpublished interviews and lectures by Dr. Gustave Jackson, an African horticultural researcher, who has acted as a consultant to the project and also teaches on it.

from an isolated and artificial style of living to one that includes shared, natural benefits. In the movement from an insular to a group membership position, the patients have reported an increase in their sense of personal pride and hope for dealing with the future" (Cornille *et al*, 1987, p. 6).

4 The mechanisms of therapeutic horticulture

Restorative environments

The influences which appear to underpin therapeutic horticulture are those of nature itself as a restorative function. Environmental psychology has provided much information about the restorative qualities of natural environments and both cognitive (reasoned) and evolutionary (inherited) components may be present. Recent research has been carried out from two main perspectives; Rachel and Stephen Kaplan have investigated the fatigue of attention and its restoration by the natural environment, whilst Roger Ulrich and his colleagues have studied the role of the natural environment in the recovery from stress.

Kaplan and Kaplan (1989) have examined in detail the preference for different landscape images and have developed the concept of a *'restorative environment'* which plays a significant role in the recovery from mental fatigue. The foundations of their research lie in the work of William James (1892; quoted in Kaplan & Kaplan, 1989, pp. 179-180) on involuntary and voluntary attention, although the Kaplans prefer the term *directed* attention in place of *voluntary*. They argue that mental fatigue arises as a result of the effort involved in inhibiting competing influences when attention is directed towards a specific task. The view or experience of nature which is inherently interesting or stimulating invokes involuntary attention which requires no effort and is therefore restorative. This idea is generally referred to as 'Attention Restoration Theory'.

They discuss the components of restorative experience in terms of *being away, fascination, extent and compatibility*. These are presented within the context of healing gardens in a later publication (Kaplan and Kaplan, 1990) and can be summarised as follows:

Being away: the sense of escape from a part of life that is ordinarily present and not always preferred. This involves a conceptual change and not necessarily a physical change:

> "Being away, at least in principle, frees one from mental activity that requires directed attention support to keep going...A new or different environment, while potentially helpful, is not essential. A change in the direction of one's gaze, or even an old environment viewed in a new way can provide the necessary conceptual shift" (Kaplan, 1995, p. 173).

Fascination: this is a direct derivation of James' involuntary attention, it is the ability for something to hold attention without the use of effort and whilst this is in play directed attention should be able to rest. Fascination can be derived from *process* – the act of carrying out an activity; or from *content* – the intrinsic substance of what is experienced (for example the landscape itself).

Extent: the aspect of an environment that provides the feeling of being "in a whole other world" that is meaningful and well-ordered:

> "It (a restorative environment) must provide enough to see, experience, and think about so that it takes up a substantial portion of the available room in one's head" (Kaplan, 1995, p. 173).

Compatibility: an affinity with the environment or activity so that a great directed attention is not required in order to engage with it, "the setting must fit what one is trying to do and what one would like to do" (Kaplan, 1995, p. 173).

Hard and soft fascination, attention recovery and reflection

Kaplan and Kaplan (1989) propose that the recovery of directed attention is not the only benefit of restorative environments, they can also provide the opportunity for thought about immediate and unresolved personal problems and reflection on larger life issues. Different restorative settings can, therefore, provide differing degrees of attention recovery and opportunities for reflection, depending on the nature of the fascination involved.

Kaplan (1995) suggests that fascination as a concept can range in quality from 'hard' to 'soft'. 'Hard' fascination is so intense that it entirely dominates attention and leaves little or no room for thinking whilst 'soft' fascination exerts a moderate hold on attention and so allows opportunity for 'reflection'. Herzog et al (1997) suggest 'amusement parks, rock concerts, bars, video games and parties' as examples of settings for hard fascination whilst natural environments are settings for soft fascination (Kaplan, 1995; Herzog et al, 1997).

Herzog et al (1997) conducted a study on student volunteers to determine the preferred settings for attention recovery and reflection. The volunteers were asked to rate the suitability of environments (ranging from urban, sports/entertainment and natural) for recovering their abilities to concentrate after a long and demanding intellectual task ('attentional recovery'), and for allowing them to resolve a serious personal problem ('reflection'). Natural settings had a high perceived score for both attentional recovery and reflection, whilst urban settings had a low score for both. Sports/entertainment settings were perceived to be intermediate but had a higher score for attentional recovery than for reflection. Thus the benefit which a restorative setting can provide may

depend on its power to cause directed attention to rest and on the opportunity for reflection to take place:

> "According to ART (Attention Restoration Theory), not all restorative settings provide both types of benefits because restoration is not just a matter of resting directed attention. The depth and quality of restoration depends on how attention is rested. In turn, that depends on the kind of fascination engaged by a restorative setting. Sports/entertainment settings primarily engage hard fascination which fills the mind and leaves little room for reflection. Thus, the quality of the restorative experience is limited. Ordinary natural settings primarily engage soft fascination which does not completely take over the mind. Soft fascination allows directed attention to rest, leaves room for reflection, and provides an esthetic buffer against painful thoughts that may accompany reflection" (Herzog et al, 1997, p. 166).

It is easy to imagine how working in a garden can engage soft fascination and leave room for reflection. The almost effortless attention to the task in hand whether weeding, hoeing or sowing, whilst pondering some deeper question is likely to be a state experienced by most gardeners.

Attentional fatigue in major illness

Research has shown that attentional fatigue can occur in major illnesses such as cancer. Using a battery of psychological tests Cimprich (1992) observed such fatigue in a group of 32 women following surgery for breast cancer. This was independent of the scale of surgery carried out. In a subsequent study (Cimprich, 1993) she showed that carrying out a 'restorative activity' which was identified and chosen with the help of a researcher could restore the attention deficit. The activities were identified with the help of a standard protocol:

> "Activities that are thought to be especially helpful in resting and restoring the ability to

concentrate involve experiencing nature in some way, for example, sitting or walking in the natural environment (backyard, garden, park) observing a natural view (trees, clouds, a sunset) tending green living things of all kinds (gardens, flowers, plants)" (Cimprich, 1993, p. 87).

The women agreed to carry out their chosen activity for 20-30 minutes at least three times per week during a three month period by signing a formal contract to that effect. Signing the contract appeared to strengthen their commitment to this routine. Those women in the group carrying out 'restorative activities' showed a significantly greater improvement in total attention score over the 90 day study period compared with the control group.

Unruh, Smith and Scammell (2000) carried out semi-structured interviews with three women who had breast cancer and used gardening as a leisure activity. The themes elicited in the interviews appeared to be consistent with a restorative effect of the gardening activity and the natural environment:

> "These interviews with gardeners who have cancer were consistent with the perspective of attention restoration theory. The gardens had the qualities of fascination, being away, extent and compatibility. They frequently helped these women to escape from the worry of cancer and to feel renewed to face it again when they returned" (Unruh, Smith and Scammell, 2000, p. 75).

The benefits of gardening

The psychological benefits of gardening were studied by Kaplan (1973) who grouped gardening satisfaction into three categories, *tangible benefits* – e.g. the monetary savings derived from growing one's own vegetables; *primary garden experiences* – the desire to work in soil, wanting to see things grow, liking being outside and an interest in learning about gardening; and what they called *sustained interest* which reflected some of the *fascinations* associated with gardening but which included few specific references to gardening itself. It included such benefits as, "diversion from routine", "valuable way to spend time", "opportunity to relax", and "ability to sustain interest" (Kaplan, 1973, p. 153). This last theme has been developed into the component of *fascination* mentioned above in the context of attention restoration theory.

In a subsequent study of members of the American Horticultural Society (4,297 replies) and readers of an organic gardening magazine (*Organic Gardening and Farming*, 240 replies) Kaplan explored further the meaning and importance of derived satisfaction from gardening and compare differences between the groups (see: Kaplan, 1983, pp. 149-153). The aspects of satisfaction that were observed can be summarised as follows:

Peacefulness and quiet – the sense of tranquillity that gardening offers was ranked as being the most important benefit.

Nature fascination was among the most important aspects and included a variety of topics which were deemed to be responsible for holding the attention of the gardener. These included active aspects of gardening such as working with the soil; more passive ones such as observing the progress of the plants and intellectual aspects associated with planning the garden.

Sensory benefits – enjoyment of the sensations offered by the garden by its beauty, colours and smells.

Tangible benefits – these are the obvious physical benefits of gardening and have been mentioned above (Kaplan and Kaplan, 1990, pp.239-240).

These themes are repeated, in many guises, throughout the literature on therapeutic horticulture.

Preference for natural landscapes

Roger Ulrich has collected much empirical and experimental data on the preference for different types of landscape and on the effects of landscape (or representations of landscape) on recovery from physical and psychological stress.

In a much cited study Ulrich showed that patients recovering form cholecystectomy (gall bladder surgery) fared better if they had a view of trees from their hospital bed than if that view was of a brick wall (Ulrich 1984).

Using two groups of 23 patients (matched as closely as possible) he found that the group which had the view of trees from their window spent significantly less time in hospital, required fewer doses of analgesics and received fewer "negative evaluative comments in nurses' notes" than the group which had a view of a brick wall from their beds. This study suggests that a landscape view can act as a stimulus to invoke involuntary attention and thereby distract the patient from their condition. However, caution needs to be applied in extrapolating the results to other patient groups or inferring that a landscape view *per se* is inherently therapeutic. This caution is described by Ulrich as follows:

> "Although the findings suggest that the natural scene had comparatively therapeutic influences, it should be recognized that the "built" view in this study was a comparatively monotonous one, a largely featureless brick wall. The conclusions cannot be extended to all built views, nor to other patient groups, such as long-term patients, who may suffer from low arousal or boredom rather than from the anxiety problems typically associated with surgeries. Perhaps to a chronically understimulated patient, a built view such as a lively city street might be more therapeutic than many natural views" (Ulrich 1984, p. 421).

In a 1991 study on stress recovery Ulrich *et al* (1991) observed that following the viewing of a stressful film (on safety with scenes of simulated injury) there was a fast recovery in physiological variables including heart rate and EMG (electromyogram) in subjects who subsequently viewed a video of natural scenes compared to those

who watched scenes of traffic or a pedestrian mall. This was consistent with his earlier work (Ulrich, 1983) which suggested that the initial response to a natural environment is the result of rapid changes in the physiological and psychological state:

> "Ulrich (1983) postulates that immediate, unconsciously triggered and initiated emotional responses – not 'controlled' cognitive responses – play a central role in the initial level of responding to nature, and have major influences on attention, subsequent conscious processing, physiological responding and behavior..." (Ulrich *et al*, 1991, pp. 207-208).

Ulrich's view is that the effect of the natural landscape and nature itself is evolutionary in origin and not predominantly cognitive or reasoned as the work of the Kaplans suggests. He sees *compatibility*, for example, as an elaborate and complex function dependent on an individual's inclinations and experience and not an innate, instinctive response. Ulrich argues that since the process of evolution took place in a natural environment it favoured those individuals who positively responded to that environment:

> "In an earlier theoretical section it was proposed that the rewards associated with natural settings during human evolution have been sufficiently critical to favour individuals who quickly and easily learned, and persistently retained, two related types of adaptive positive responding to nature: restoration following stress or taxing activities; and in the absence of stress, positive emotional/attentional/approach responses to nature contents and configurations, especially those that favored well-being or survival because of such advantages as high food potential and low risk" (Ulrich *et al*, 1991, p. 226).

One aspect of this could be the rapid recovery in the natural (restorative) setting from the effects of stressful stimuli, seen by Ulrich. Although the Kaplans' attention restoration theory and Ulrich's theory of recovery from stress appear to be at odds with one another, Kaplan (1995) proposed a model which integrated attention fatigue within the stress mechanism. In this model attention fatigue can lead to the stress response; it can occur as a result of the stress response; or it can occur alongside the stress response as a result of an aversive stimulus. It is likely, therefore, that a number of complex psychological mechanisms are involved during the process of stress and attention fatigue and are at work within 'restorative environments' and experiences. These mechanisms may explain why horticulture and gardening are popular in rehabilitation even though other activities may well provide opportunities for the development of manual dexterity, group and social skills and other skills. Thus the preference for a natural environment, and interaction with it in the form of agriculture, horticulture or gardening may stem from our evolutionary origins and also from learned cultural influences.

5 Messages and themes from research: towards a synthesis

The literature survey described in the preceding sections has been concerned with the use of horticulture for specific groups of individuals. The final section examined the underlying psychological mechanisms which may be involved in the benefits derived from experience of the natural environment and from participation in horticulture. A number of threads and themes run throughout the studies examined. It is evident from the literature that the benefits of participation in therapeutic horticulture, the intended outcomes of specific projects, and the conditions necessary to achieve those outcomes depend in many cases on the client group concerned. The following sections summarise the themes and briefly review the evidence on benefits and outcomes, and also the needs of particular client groups.

Social inclusion

'Social inclusion', as a concept or outcome of horticulture and gardening, has not been referred to explicitly in the texts reviewed here. However, it is possible to infer from some of these studies that social inclusion can, and will, be a positive outcome for some groups of people participating in gardening projects. We use a working definition of social *exclusion* provided by the Centre for the Analysis of Social Exclusion at the London School of Economics and Political Sciences (LSE):

> "An individual is socially excluded if he or she does not participate in key activities of the society in which he or she lives" (Burchardt *et al*, 2002, p. 30).

Consequently social *inclusion* refers to the processes by which people are enabled to participate in these key activities. Burchardt *et al* (2002) identify four dimensions of inclusion: *consumption, production,* *social interaction* and political *engagement*.

■ Consumption is the idea of being able to buy the sorts of goods and services that other people can buy, and access the types of public services that other people can access.

■ Production is the idea of being engaged in a socially valuable activity, including paid work, education/training, child care, other unpaid work and voluntary work.

■ Social interaction refers to social networks and cultural identity.

■ Political engagement is broadly conceived to include notions of self-determination, 'having a say', empowerment, being involved in campaigning organisations and so on.

It is clear from the evidence reviewed here that each of these four dimensions of social inclusion can be outcomes of social and therapeutic horticulture. The extent to which these dimensions are influenced by gardening will vary from group to group, so for example, gardening may promote social interaction among older people while the production dimension can be addressed by gardening programmes seeking to provide employment, work discipline, development of skills and socially useful activities. Not all four dimensions will necessarily be promoted or maintained through any one individual gardening project. However, even where just one dimension of social inclusion is addressed then this can be a positive outcome for participants.

The extent to which social inclusion is promoted through gardening and horticulture is a major theme of the *Growing Together* project (of which this review is a part) and will be investigated and explored in greater detail in future research and publications. The message from existing research suggests that social inclusion, particularly the four dimensions discussed above, can be promoted successfully, either individually or collectively, through social and therapeutic horticulture. Many of the themes summarised below, and the benefits of gardening, are also closely related to the concept of social inclusion.

Employment

One of the functions that defines most people within society and appears to support physical and mental health is employment. Warr (1987), for example, proposed a model containing nine determinants of mental health which he likened to vitamins and which could be obtained through employment. These included the opportunity for skill use, variety, social contact and a valued social position. Absence or deficiency in these 'vitamins' could lead to poorer physical and mental health and would seriously undermine a person's feeling of self-worth, self-esteem and value to society. This is particularly so with individuals with disabilities or enduring illness, especially mental ill health. Many of these give up hope of ever achieving employment, leading to a consequent decline in their state and further

reduction in their quality of life. Many horticultural projects have been designed specifically with the goal of assisting their participants eventually to gain employment, whilst others recognise the importance of employment and offer an activity which is a substitute for it with a sense of order, structure and discipline.

The particular groups where employment is a significant issue are those with learning difficulties, mental health problems and ex-offenders. Employment arising from projects for offenders and individuals with mental health problems has also been mentioned in previous sections.

Dehart-Bennett and Relf (1990) have reviewed issues surrounding the employment of adults with learning difficulties in the US horticultural industry. They discuss the work showing that disabled adults can contribute successfully to this sector of employment. They also reported that in general the attitude of employers was positive and the authors conclude:

> "The responses indicate that a large portion of the ornamental horticulture industry has a positive perception of the work abilities of these individuals and may offer them employment opportunities. Sixty percent of the employers agreed that these individuals could perform tasks in entry-level skills. If these skills are targeted in horticultural vocational training, then it appears that workers with mental retardation will have a marketable job skill" (Dehart-Bennett and Relf, 1990, p. 14).

Dobbs and Relf (1991, 1995) examined the employment of individuals with learning disabilities on university grounds maintenance crews, either individually or as groups (enclaves) contracted from a rehabilitation workshop. They suggest that being part of an 'enclave' may be of particular benefit to the individuals:

> "Within an enclave, an IMD [Individual with Mental Disabilities] may have the ideal situation

for permanent, year round employment or may serve as a temporary employee during the peak growing season. In the latter case, it would be the responsibility of the sheltered workshop to develop contracts for employment in other fields during the grounds maintenance non- peak season (for example, contracting to pot bedding plants for a greenhouse business in late winter). However, this would still insure that the individuals had employment and structure throughout the year" (Dobbs and Relf, 1995, 239).

In the UK Sharples and Galvin (1995) and Aish and Israel (2001) have studied the Sheltered Work Opportunities Project (SWOP) for people with mental health problems (see also Davies, 2000). This project is based at a nursery on the south coast and propagates and sells shrubs to wholesalers, local authorities, nurseries, garden centres and landscape gardeners. Although its sales contribute to the running costs it is still partially dependent on donations. Aish and Israel (2001) examined the records of 100 participants of the project and found that 49% who left the project went into either employment or training with 20% going into full time employment and 26% taking up paid employment of some kind. They also found that participants spent considerably less time in hospital (86% less) whilst participating in the project than they did prior to attending. The saving on the hospital admission costs was estimated to be 2.75 million pounds over ten years.

Thus participation in horticulture programmes can provide the training and skills for outside employment; the project or programme may itself provide the employment; or it may provide structured work which is unpaid but serves as a substitute for paid employment. In each case the programmes help to provide the benefits associated with work.

'Race' and Gender

The participation of ethnic minorities in community gardening in the US has been studied, but research on the involvement of racial and ethnic minorities in gardening programmes in the UK is lacking. A number of garden projects have, however, been described and these identify some of the needs of the groups and areas in which horticulture may be of benefit to them. Some of these groups may face discrimination or social exclusion because of their ethnicity, their gender and also because they are made more vulnerable by illness. For example, the project 'Gardening for Health' was set up in Bradford in response to the fact that Asian women are at a particularly high risk of coronary heart disease. The project encourages community participation, physical activity, healthy eating and relaxation, whilst offering relief from isolation and social support for inner city Bangladeshi women (see Crouch, Sempik and Wiltshire, 2001). The Black Environment Network (www.ben-network.org.uk) also lists garden projects carried out by black and ethnic minority participants but these, like the previous project, have not been studied in detail.

There is some indication in the literature that gender may be an important consideration in terms of how individuals experience horticulture, landscape and wilderness. The inclusion of women in gender specific research, for example, has been a feature of a small number of studies. However, the authors of some of these surveys have identified gender issues as 'chance' outcomes of their research. Other studies have included women serendipitously because of the predominance in particular populations. In only a small number of cases have women been included purposively as subjects for primary investigation.

Unruh *et al* (2000) were interested in patients' experiences of gardening as therapy following treatment for cancer. As the nature of their particular area of study only included women, i.e. those who had undergone treatment for breast cancer, they concluded that gender could also be a significant factor in how individuals experience horticulture:

> "These participants were also women and their reflections about gardening and experiences with cancer may be more characteristic of

women. Men who garden may raise different issues" (Unruh et al, 2000, p.76).

Women were included in Kuo and Sullivan's (2001) research into the effects of landscape view among the residents of urban apartments because of the predominance of women in the population, i.e. because "official adult residents in urban public housing are overwhelmingly female" (Kuo and Sullivan, 2001, p. 552). They also 'matched' interviewees with three women interviewers by gender.

Powch's wilderness therapy work with women survivors of sexual abuse initially only included women serendipitously:

> "I began talking with women who had experienced the wilderness as healing – survivors of sexual abuse, women who work with survivors and women who, like myself, are 'merely' survivors of the patriarchal context in which we were raised" (Powch, 1994, p. 12).

However, Powch later confirmed her intent to include only women in her research on wilderness therapy because:

> "It has been important to me to include the voices of women of color and other marginalized groups of women" (Powch, 1994, p. 13).

Powch then began looking for an additional 'ingredient' in her research that was empowering for women. She concluded that notions of unity and female solidarity were distinct outcomes for women who shared wilderness therapy. She further suggested that feminist spirituality and creativity were enhanced by women's collective experiences of the wilderness:

> "Wilderness therapy appears to be a promising vehicle for empowerment of women. Its promise is not limited to being a vehicle by which women can master skills that enhance self-

esteem and a sense of control. Its promise is much greater and goes beyond the personal when it is connected with the feminist spirituality movement and reclamation of the earth as a woman's place, woman as creator and a part of the spirit of the earth" (Powch, 1994, p.25).

Frederickson and Anderson's (1999) purposive study of women's experiences of wilderness therapy described positive outcomes for women in terms of increased equanimity, cohesion and the escape from stereotype. The authors also suggested that integral to an all women wilderness group were elements of personal bonding and emotional safety.

There is little suggestion in the literature more generally that the benefits of social and therapeutic horticulture to people who are ill, disabled or socially excluded relate particularly to issues of gender. However, the small number of studies that have purposively included women in their respondent groups have emphasised some interesting outcomes in terms of the ways in which women with particular needs and experiences encounter wilderness, landscape and horticulture.

Physical activity and exercise

The association of exercise and physical activity with health is well known, and research also suggests that physical exercise can be useful in the treatment of mental health problems such as anxiety and depression (for a review see Burbach, 1997). Intense exercise has been used in the treatment of patients with Alzheimer's disease. Lindenmuth and Moose (1990) showed that the cognitive abilities of elderly Alzheimer's patients can be substantially and significantly improved by a programme of physical exercise. They attributed this to an improvement in cardiovascular factors and 'emotional stimulation' (increased sensory input). Although they did not use gardening as the activity for physical exercise it is possible to see how gardening could be used to provide the same degree of physical exertion as an exercise programme.

There has recently been a move to promote outdoor conservation activities such as tree planting, hedge laying and habitat restoration as forms of exercise to improve physical and mental health. These programmes have been set up in conjunction with the British Trust for Conservation Volunteers and have been called 'Green Gyms'. At present 5 such Green Gyms operate in the UK and their objectives are to improve both physical and mental health and well-being in a natural setting. Recent research has shown significant improvement in measures of cardiovascular fitness and mental health.

A pilot study of the first Green Gym project (Reynolds, 1999) showed an improvement in the muscle strength (grip strength) of participants which, the author notes, may be of particular benefit to older participants. The level of exertion during Green Gym activities was sufficient to elevate heart rate to levels which could provide cardiovascular 'training':

> "The heart rate recordings show that levels of between 60% and 80% of estimated maximum heart rates are attained and sustained for periods of between 20 and 45 minutes. This level of intensity and duration would, if performed regularly, be sufficient to elicit a 'training effect'. In particular, activities using large muscle groups in a rhythmic manner such as raking, appear to elevate the heart rate to an appropriate level for sustained periods of time" (Reynolds, 1999, p. 41).

Data obtained during interviews with participants showed that they perceived the Green Gym as beneficial to their mental health and well-being. There was also a significant improvement in measured Scores of 'General Health Perception' and 'Role Limitation Due to Physical Problems' assessed by questionnaire (see: Reynolds, 1999, Appendix II).

Reynolds (2002) also carried out a longitudinal[7] study of 37 participants of another Green Gym programme. Many (30%) were unemployed and a large number (44%) also reported anxiety and depression. She found a significant improvement in

the mental health score (SF-12, see Reynolds, 2002, Appendix 1) and a downward trend in the score of depression using the 'Hospital Anxiety and Depression Scale' (see Reynolds, 2002, p. 31). A small number of participants also showed a significant improvement in fitness and the group showed a trend towards weight loss. Interviews with ten participants in the programme revealed that social aspects of the group were important and were mentioned by seven of those interviewed. The environmental setting of the Green Gym was a recurring theme in the interviews and may be important both for the perceived benefits and also for maintaining the compliance and motivation of the participants. Indeed, in her study of the first Green Gym programme Reynolds (1999) suggests the possible role of the 'Biophilia Effect' in the programme. The 'Biophilia Hypothesis' was advanced by Wilson (1984) and suggests that human beings possess an innate attraction to nature (see also: Kellert and Wilson, 1993). This attraction may explain both the benefits and appeal of the natural environment and activities associated with it.

Food

At one time the principal purpose of allotments and community gardens was to provide food at low cost to those in need. In some cases this is still true today, however, many gardeners grow fruit and vegetables for the sheer satisfaction of home production and for production of unusual varieties or under specific conditions such as organic or permaculture. Indeed, there is a vast industry supplying seeds, tools and publications to the amateur vegetable grower. So it is not surprising that growing and harvesting of food is seen as important in some of the studies on social and therapeutic horticulture mentioned in previous sections.

In her survey of community gardens in New York Armstrong (2000) found that one of the most commonly expressed reasons for participation was access to fresh and better tasting foods. Producing food was seen as a component of self-esteem in Waliczek's survey of community gardeners (Waliczek

---

[7] A 'longitudinal' study involves measurements taken over a period of time.

et al, 1996) and was valued more highly than actually saving money (significantly different satisfaction score).

Seller, Fieldhouse and Phelan (1999) noted that "taking home fresh vegetables" (p.292) was one of the main aspects of work on allotments that people with mental health problems liked the most.

Kaplan's study of the psychological benefits of gardening (Kaplan, 1973) showed that gardeners valued tangible results of their labours such as the enjoyment of producing food, reducing expenditure and harvesting food.

What is surprising is that the themes of food cultivation, preparation and consumption were not explored to a greater extent within these studies especially considering that growing food as a hobby receives so much interest. The unanswered question (and to some extent the 'unasked' question) is whether the growing of food, and its preparation and consumption, has a special meaning, and whether that special meaning contributes to the beneficial effects of social and therapeutic horticulture. It is interesting in this respect to note that Waliczek et al (1996) considered growing food under the category of esteem needs and not under the physiological needs as defined by Maslow (1943). There is a great deal of scope for further work in this area.

Social cohesion

For patients with mental ill health the cohesion and social interaction brought about by gardening projects appear to be significant outcomes. Horticulture programmes enable and facilitate group working and this in turn appears to promote social cohesion and the development of social and communication skills. In some projects this has been one of the intended goals whilst in others social cohesion appears to have occurred simply as a result of the dynamics of the group and the situation. It is interesting to note that research carried out using the Oxford Happiness Inventory suggests that participation in cooperative activities is associated with happiness. In a longitudinal study Lu and Argyle

(1991, quoted in Argyle, Martin and Lu, 1995) found that 'Cooperativeness' was a predictor of later happiness. An analysis of their Cooperativeness scale showed that 'Cooperation in Joint Activities' was the factor that best predicted happiness. Furthermore, in their review of the use of the Oxford Happiness Inventory, Argyle, Martin and Lu (1995) describe the reported association between social skills and happiness:

> "To summarise, the following social skills have been found to be associated with happiness, and in most cases there is evidence that this is a causal relationship:
>
> Assertiveness
> Cooperativeness
> Verbal Skills
> Nonverbal Skills
> Friendship Skills
> Relationship Skills
>
> Lack of Social Anxiety or Self-Consciousness" (Argyle, Martin and Lu, 1995, pp. 178-179).

Many of these skills develop as a result of participation in social and therapeutic horticulture and are the intended outcomes of many horticulture programmes. It is perhaps possible to speculate that development of these skills and any subsequent elevation of mood is particularly important in clients suffering from mental ill health.

The amelioration of Alzheimer's Disease

The physical design of the garden for patients with Alzheimer's disease appears to be of particular importance. It is a place of refuge for patients and needs to have a distinct boundary which separates it from the outside environment. The significance of the walled garden as a metaphor for paradise has already been discussed. The layout and location of the garden has to be such that it can be used readily without causing confusion and frustration to the patients. It needs to be safe so that no harm befalls those who use it who are likely to have difficulties with both physical and cognitive function. It is a source of sensory stimulation in terms of colour, smell, texture and can stimulate emotion and positive feelings and memories. However, the level of sensory input and its manner of use needs to be managed and the matching of specific garden designs and activities to particular stages of the disease has been proposed.

Acceptance of responsibility and control

The acceptance of responsibility by older people appears to be a significant factor in slowing down deterioration of their physical and mental condition. The care of gardens and plants may be a useful mechanism for providing older people with that sense of responsibility and with the opportunity to make decisions.

In an elegant controlled experiment Langer and Rodin (1976) showed that residents of a nursing home in Connecticut who were given a degree of decision-making responsibility for themselves fared better than those residents in a control group who relied on staff for decisions. The patients were assessed by individual questionnaires administered to them directly and by questionnaires to the nursing staff assessing each patient. There was a significant improvement in the 'responsibility group' of perceived happiness and activity, and of reported social interaction and alertness:

> "It appears that inducing a greater sense of personal responsibility in people who may have virtually relinquished decision making, either by choice or necessity, produces improvement. In the present investigation, patients in the comparison group were given a communication stressing the staff's desire to make them happy and were otherwise treated in the sympathetic manner characteristic of this high-quality nursing home. Despite the care provided for these people, 71% were rated as having become more debilitated over a period as short as 3 weeks. In contrast with this group, 93% of

the people who were encouraged to make decisions for themselves, given decisions to make, and given responsibility for something outside of themselves, actually showed overall improvement. Based on their own judgements and by the judgements of the nurses with whom they interacted on a daily basis, they became more active and felt happier. Perhaps more important was the judged improvement in their mental alertness and increased behavioural involvement in many different kinds of activities" (Langer and Rodin, 1976, p. 197).

At around the same time, Schulz (1976) reported that elderly residents of a retirement home who had control over the frequency and duration of visits they received from college student volunteers, or where the visits were predictable (i.e. they were notified of the time and duration of the visits) showed greater physical and psychological well-being in a battery of tests than those residents who received no visits or random visits. He concluded that predictability and the exercise of control were significant factors in slowing down the psychological and physical deterioration of aging.

Control of anger and frustration

As previously mentioned in the context of horticulture and offenders, experience of the natural environment has been shown to reduce aggression. The research cited in this review suggests that gardening and horticulture activities can also be used to control anger and frustration by the acceptance of 'delayed gratification' through training and experience. Participants of training programmes learn to accept that the fruits of horticulture are not immediate but take time to grow and mature. This then leads to a frame of mind in which the trainee does not always seek immediate gratification in all aspects of life but is content or able to wait for reward:

The work of Hirschi (1969) has also shown that success and desire for education and training may reduce the likelihood of delinquency in adolescents. The training programme described by Flagler (1995) reinforces the recognition of success with the award of a certificate, and as Flagler points out for some this is the first certificate of achievement that they have ever received.

A metaphor and model for life

Horticulture has been used by many writers as a metaphor for the process of life, where there is reproduction, growth, ageing and death. One generation succeeds another, which in turn is succeeded by the next. These processes can be seen as entirely natural and non-threatening and for children they can serve as starting points for discussions of real-life issues such as relationships and bereavement.

> "Two subjects that in many contexts are perceived as threatening are death and sex. However, death whether a flat [seed-tray] of seedlings lost to damping-off or a flower fading from its peak of beauty is an integral part of horticulture and must be dealt with on a continuous basis. Likewise, plant propagation, both sexual and asexual, is a part of many horticultural activities. Encountering these topics in horticultural therapy may bring forth opportunities for discussions that can ultimately lead to communications and insights in the far more complex areas of human death and human sexuality" (Relf, 1981, p. 147).

Spiritual aspects of horticulture

For many people gardening and the experience of gardens and landscape has a spiritual dimension. Unruh (1997) suggests that there are three broad themes with spiritual implications in "garden musings". These are "reflections about oneself as a solitary being", "reflections about the life cycle and one's place in it" and "gardening as a spiritual expression of community". This spiritual dimension can vary from the appreciation of nature and wonderment through to the feelings of prayer and communion with God.

The Quiet Garden Movement, for example, is particularly concerned with spiritual aspects of the experience of gardens and was established as a network of gardens, mainly in private houses, for "prayer, silence, reflection and the appreciation of beauty" within a predominantly Christian context:

> "Irrespective of its size and appearance, in the garden we are in touch with our natural roots in the recurring cycle of growth, decay, death and new growth. And at a level of which we are usually largely unaware, this natural process then enters the realm of the spirit, giving us that sense of healing, of restoration, which we do not need to define to admit" (Boardman, 2001, p. 20).

Spiritual experiences of gardening have also been encountered by researchers observing gardening in secular settings. For example in a study of two gardening projects for older people Heliker, Chadwick, and O'Connell (2000) observed that many of the participants likened gardening to a prayer and spoke of it as a way of relating to God. This spiritual theme did not appear to be associated with any level of education, socio-economic status, culture or background. Unruh, Smith and Scammell (2000) also reported a spiritual dimension to gardening in two women suffering from breast cancer. Intuitively, one would expect that a spiritual component would be more likely to be present in these two groups, i.e. older persons and those suffering from major or life-threatening illness, since these groups are more likely to reflect on their own mortality than other groups participating in horticultural programmes. This may be the case but the research presented on wilderness programmes suggests that other groups may also undergo a spiritual experience in response to nature.

A model of activities, processes and outcomes

From our examination of the literature on social and therapeutic horticulture and the associated work concerned with environmental psychology we have prepared a simple model (shown in Figure 1) which shows the main activities, processes and outcomes as drawn from the available evidence. At the base of the model lie the underlying foundations which determine the inherent appeal of the natural environment. The origin of this appeal is still under debate. It may be evolutionary; it may be learned or acquired. But whatever its nature it supports both the passive appreciation of landscape and the active participation in horticulture and gardening. Within the divisions of 'active' and 'passive' there are many processes and activities which are inter-related and which provide rehabilitation, acceptance and inclusion on one side and tranquillity, peace and spirituality on the other. These are represented as two distinct groupings - but nonetheless connected. The reason for separate groups is that the former, rehabilitation, acceptance and inclusion are frequently the goals of active programmes whilst passive appreciation of nature is often associated with tranquillity, peace and spirituality. This division is not a 'hard and fast' rule of any sort but an attempt to show the diversity of the aims of different programmes. The two groups of attributes are shown to be interconnected as one can lead to the other and vice versa. In most cases this exchange is desirable and intended; acceptance and inclusion should lead to peace and tranquillity; and peace and tranquillity can be the steps to acceptance, inclusion and rehabilitation. The final component of the model are health and well-being, at its summit. This is the ultimate goal of social and therapeutic horticulture and represents a major part of all interpretations of 'quality of life'.

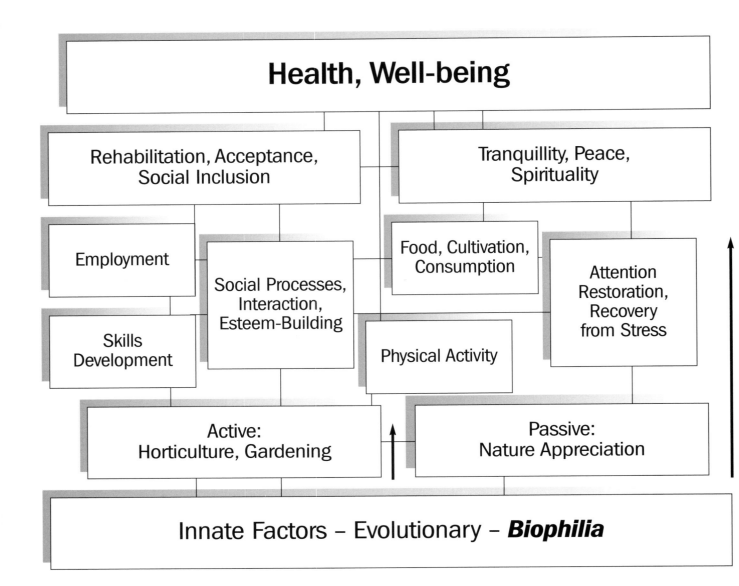

Figure 1 Health and Well-being Through Nature and Horticulture:
a simple model of some of the processes, activities and outcomes of social and therapeutic horticulture as described in the literature showing the interconnectedness of all elements.

Conclusion

The data presented in this literature review provide evidence for the effectiveness of horticulture and gardening in a number of different therapeutic settings. Experimental evidence from environmental psychology also supports a theoretical framework for therapeutic horticulture. Even though this evidence does exist there is a need for more research and the authors of this review acknowledge the observations of previous writers who have highlighted the scant amount of 'hard evidence' that exists in support of therapeutic horticulture. Although a substantial body of literature has been added since Markee and Janick's extensive literature survey of 1978 much of this does not include experimental or empirical results – an observation that the previous authors made almost a quarter of a century ago.

It was surprising, and also disappointing to see the number of reports which were published as 'pilot studies' or 'preliminary results' and which were not followed up with the full research findings. It is possible that some of this work has been presented as theses and dissertations and is available in university and college libraries but such locations can be difficult and expensive to access for practitioners carrying out research outside a university environment. Indeed, it was intended that publications reviewed here should be reasonably accessible and therefore dissertations and theses did not form a large part of this review. Those workers who carry out research as part of academic study should be encouraged to publish their findings in journals and magazines, and those practitioners engaged in teaching should be instrumental in coaching their students in the practice of research and writing.

There is also the need for the publication of data in 'mainstream' medical, scientific, social sciences and horticultural journals. This will serve two main functions. Firstly, it will bring the field of therapeutic horticulture to the attention of medical professionals and those engaged in local and central government. If it is seen as an effective and useful (and also cost-effective) addition to more 'conventional' therapy then it will find a place in the various government and local authority strategies that are regularly produced for improving health, well-being and social inclusion. The consequence of this should be reflected in an appropriate level of funding and support for therapeutic horticulture.

Secondly, publication of papers in 'mainstream' academic and professional journals maintains the high quality of research and writing that is needed in a field seeking to establish its identity as a part of a modern and professional health and social care agenda.

Many of the effects of social and therapeutic horticulture, and other adjunctive therapies, are subtle and are influenced by other factors. It is, therefore, difficult to disentangle the benefits of horticulture from the effects of associated activities and processes. Work is needed for the creation and evaluation of a sensitive and reliable methodology for carrying out research in this field as many of the approaches used in 'mainstream' medical research, such as randomised controlled trials, may be too expensive and arguably inappropriate. There has been progress in this area. Unruh *et al* (2000) used the 'Perceived Restorativeness Scale' devised by Hartig and his colleagues at Goteborg University in Sweden (see Unruh *et al*, 2000) and this is currently under further development.

Research methods from different disciplines such as environmental psychology have also been applied to horticulture-related activities, notably by Professor Roger Ulrich and his colleagues at Texas A & M University. Shoemaker, Relf and Lohr (2000) recently reviewed the methodology used in studying people-plant interactions so as to encourage research in this field. They advocate collaboration between horticulturalists and social and behavioural scientists to enable the sharing of expertise and also of resources such as sophisticated physiological measuring equipment.

Another indicator of the growing interest in social and therapeutic horticulture research has been the large number of abstracts (68) submitted to the recent International Horticultural Congress in Toronto (August 2002) for inclusion in the symposium 'Expanding Roles for Horticulture in Improving Well-being and Life Quality'. A number of these abstracts describe the measurement of physiological variables such as blood pressure and heart rate and in some cases also the electromyogram (EMG) and electroencephalogram (EEG)[8].

Such application of methodology and the increasing interest among researchers should provide a firm foundation of knowledge for the future. Perhaps this hope for the future is best summarised by the following words from the opening chapter of Damon Olszowy's book *Horticulture for the Disabled and Disadvantaged* published in 1978:

> "Even though horticulture and its social implications have received the least attention, the values to this aspect of horticulture are likely to influence modern society in the future. These values deal with affection, with pleasure, with beauty, and with satisfaction. It is because of some of these values and their association with healing that medicine has turned to horticulture" (Olszowy, 1978, p. 3).

---

[8] *At the time of writing of this review (October 2002) abstracts of the International Horticultural Congress are available on the Internet at: http://www.ihc2002.org/ihc2002/multi_day-symposia_S07.htm. Invited papers will be published in Acta Horticulturae.*

References

Ackley, D. and Cole, L. (1987) 'The effect of a horticultural therapy program on children with cerebral palsy', *Journal of Rehabilitation*, vol. 53, (4), pp. 70-73.

Airhart, D.L., Willis, T. and Westrick, P. (1987) 'Horticultural training for adolescent special education students', *Journal of Therapeutic Horticulture*, vol. 2, pp. 17-22.

Aish, R. and Israel, M. (2001) *Preliminary Report of a Research Project into the Effectiveness of Supported Work Rehabilitation in a Therapeutic Horticultural Environment at Cherry Tree Nursery*, Bournemouth: SWOP.

Argyle, M., Martin, M. and Lu, L. (1995) 'Testing for stress and happiness: the role of social and cognitive factors', in: *Stress and Emotion*, vol. 15, Speilberger, C.D. and Sarason, I.G. (eds), Washington: Taylor and Francis, pp. 173-187.

Armstrong, D. (2000) 'A survey of community gardens in upstate New York: implications for health promotion and community development', *Health and Place*, vol. 6, (4), pp. 319-327.

Bassett, T. (1981) 'Reaping on the margins, a century of community gardening in America', *Landscape*, vol. 25, (2), pp. 1-8.

Beckwith, M.E. and Gilster, S.D. (1997) 'The paradise garden: a model garden design for those with Alzheimer's disease', *Activities, Adaptation and Aging*, vol. 22, (1-2), pp. 3-16.

Bennett, C., So, N.K. and Smith, W.B. (1999) 'Horticultural therapy in an epilepsy clinic', *Epilepsia*, vol. 40, (Suppl. 2), pp. 107-108.

Bhatti, M. (2002) *Occasional Paper: Gardening in Later Life*, Brighton: University of Brighton.

Boardman, B. (2001) 'Restorative gardens and the world-wide quiet garden movement', in: *People, Land & Sustainability: a Global View of Community Gardening*, Ferris, J., Morris, M., Norman, C. and Sempik, J. (eds), Nottingham: The Co-operative Group and PLS, pp. 20-21.

Bradburn, N.M. and Caplovitz, D. (1965) *Reports on Happiness*, Chicago: Aldine.

Bryant, W. (1991) 'Creative group work with confused elderly people: a development of sensory integration therapy', *British Journal of Occupational Therapy*, vol. 54, (5), pp. 187-192.

Burbach, F.R. (1997) 'The efficacy of physical activity interventions within mental health services: anxiety and depressive disorders', *Journal of Mental Health*, vol. 6, (6), pp. 243-267.

Burchardt, T., Le Grand, J. and Piachaud, D. (2002) 'Degrees of Exclusion: Developing a Dynamic, Multidimensional Measure', in: *Understanding Social Exclusion*, Hills, J., Le Grand, J. and Piachaud, D. (eds), New York: Oxford University Press, pp. 30-43.

Burke, G.L., Arnold, A.M., Bild, D.E., Cushman, M., Fried, L.P., Newman, A., Nunn, C. and Robbins, J. (2001) 'Factors associated with healthy aging: the cardiovascular health study', *Journal of the American Geriatrics Society*, vol. 49, (3), pp. 254-262.

Caspersen, C., Bloemberg, B., Saris, W., Merritt, R. and Kromhout, D. (1991) 'The prevelance of selected physical activities and their relation with coronary heart disease risk factors in elderly men: the Zutphen study', *American Journal of Epidemiology*, vol. 133, pp. 1078-1092.

Cimprich, B. (1993) 'Development of an intervention to restore attention in cancer patients', *Cancer Nursing*, vol. 16, pp. 83-92.

Cimprich, B. (1992) 'Attentional fatigue following breast cancer surgery', *Research in Nursing and Health*, vol. 15, pp. 199-207.

Cohen-Mansfield, J. and Werner, P. (1998) 'Visits to an outdoor garden: impact on behavior and mood of nursing home residents who pace', *Research and Practice in Alzheimer's Disease*, pp. 419-436., Vellas, B. and Fitten, L.J. (eds), New York: Springer Publishing Company.

Cohen-Mansfield, J. and Werner, P. (1999) 'Outdoor wandering parks for persons with dementia: a survey of characteristics and use', *Alzheimer Disease and Associated Disorders*, vol. 13, (2), pp. 109-17.

Colson, J.H.C. (1944) *The Rehabilitation of the Injured*, Cassell.

Cornille, T.A., Rohrer, G.E., Phillips, S.G. and Mosier, J.G. (1987) 'Horticultural therapy in substance abuse treatment', *Journal of Therapeutic Horticulture*, vol. 2, pp. 3-8.

Coval, M., Crocket, D., Holliday, S. and Koch, W. (1985) 'A muti-focus assessment scale for use with the frail elderly populations', *Canadian Journal of Aging*, vol. 4, pp. 101-109.

Cowden, K. (1969) 'The mentally retarded can contribute', *Hospital and Community Psychiatry*, vol. 20, (12), pp. 395.

Crouch, D. and Ward, C, (1997) *The Allotment: its Landscape and Culture*, Nottingham: Five Leaves Press.

Crouch, D., Sempik, J. and Wiltshire, R. (2001) *Growing in the Community: A Good Practice Guide for the Management of Allotments*, London: LGA Publications.

Davis-Berman, J. and Berman, D.S. (1989) 'The wilderness therapy program: an empirical study of its effects with adolescents in an outpatient setting', *Journal of Contemporary Psychotherapy*, vol. 19, pp. 271-281.

de Montmollin, M.J., Zimmermann, E., Bernheim, J. and Harding, T. (1986) 'Sociotherapeutic treatment of delinquents in prison', *International Journal of Offender Therapy and Comparative Criminology*, vol. 30, (1), pp. 25-34.

DeHart-Bennett, M.E. and Relf, P.D. (1990) 'Horticultural careers for persons with mental retardation', *Journal for Vocational Special Needs Education*, vol. 12, (3), pp. 11-15.

DiPietro, L. (2001) 'Physical activity in aging: changes in patterns and their relationship to health and function', *The Journals of Gerontology, Series A, Biological Sciences and Medical Sciences*, vol. 56, (Special Issue No. 2), pp. 13-22.

Dobbs, G.S. and Relf, P.D. (1991) 'Enclave employment of disabled individuals in a university grounds maintenance department: A case report', *Journal of Therapeutic Horticulture*, vol. 6, pp. 38-48.

Dobbs, G.S. and Relf, P.D. (1995) 'Enclave employment of disabled individuals in a university grounds maintenance department: a case report', *Acta Horticulturae*, vol. 391, pp. 233-240.

Doutt, K.M., Airhart, D.L. and Willis, T. W. (1989) 'Horticultural therapy activities for exceptional children', *Journal of Therapeutic Horticulture*, vol. 4, pp. 10-14.

Doxon, L.E., Mattson, R.H. and Jurish, A.P. (1987) 'Human stress reduction through horticultural vocational training', *HortScience*, vol. 22, (4), pp. 655-656.

Ebel, S. (1991) 'Designing stage-specific horticultural therapy interventions for patient's with Alzheimer's disease', *Journal of Therapeutic Horticulture*, vol. 6, (1), pp. 3-9.

Eddy, R.T. and Sadof, C.S. (1993) 'Training persons with mental disabilities as greenhouse integrated pest management scouts', *HortTechnology*, vol. 3, pp. 459-461.

Fabrigoule, C., Letenneur, L., Dartigues, J., Zarrouk, M., Commenges, D. and Barberger-Gateau, P. (1995) 'Social and leisure activities and risk of dementia: a prospective longitudinal study', *Journal of American Geriatrics Society*, vol. 43, pp. 485-490.

Ferris, J., Morris, M., Norman, C. and Sempik, J. (eds), (2001) *People, Land & Sustainability: a Global View of Community Gardening*, Nottingham: The Co-operative Group and PLS.

Fieldhouse, J. (2003) 'The impact of an allotment group on mental health clients' well being, and social networking', *British Journal of Occupational Therapy*, (In Press).

Finch, C.R. (1995) 'Green Brigade: horticultural learn-and-earn programs for juvenile offenders', *HortTechnology*, vol. 5, (2), pp. 118-120.

Flagler, J. (1993) 'Correctional youth and the green industry', *Journal of Therapeutic Horticulture*, vol. 7, (1), pp. 49-55.

Flagler, J. (1994) 'Corrections and the green industry', in: *People-Plant Relationships: Setting Research Priorities*, Flagler, J. and Poincelot, R. P. (Eds), New York: The Food Products Press/The Haworth Press Inc., pp. 283-290.

Flagler, J. (1995) 'The role of horticulture in training correctional youth', *HortTechnology*, vol. 5, (2), pp. 185-187.

Fredrickson, L.A. and Anderson, D.H. (1999) 'A qualitative exploration of the wilderness experience as a source of spritual inspiration', *Journal of Environmental Psychology*, vol. 19, (1), pp. 21-39.

Gibson, R.B. and Hughes, M.P. (2000) 'Treatment of the sexually violent predator: a horticultural approach', *Journal of Therapeutic Horticulture*, vol. 11, pp. 20-25.

Giddan, N.S. and Giddan, S.J. (eds) (1991) *Autistic Adults at Bittersweet Farms*, New York: The Haworth Press.

Goodban, A. and Goodban, D. (1990) 'Horticultural Therapy: a growing concern, Part 1', *British Journal of Occupational Therapy*, vol. 53, (10), pp. 425-429.

Goodban, A. and Goodban, D. (1990) 'Horticultural Therapy: a growing concern, Part 2', *British Journal of Occupational Therapy*, vol. 53, (11), pp. 468-470.

Growth Point, (1999) 'Your future starts here: practitioners determine the way ahead', *Growth Point*, vol. 79, pp. 4-5.

Gurel, L., Linn, M.W., Linn, B.S., Davis, J.E. Jr. and Maroney, R.S. (1979) 'Patients in nursing homes: multi-disciplinary characteristics and outcomes', *Journal of the American Medical Association*, vol. 23, pp. 390-400.

Heliker, D., Chadwick, A. and O'Connell, T. (2000) 'The meaning of gardening and the effects on perceived well being of a gardening project on diverse populations of elders', *Activities, Adaptation & Aging*, vol. 25, (3), pp. 35-57.

Herzog, T.R., Black, A.M., Fountaine, K.A. and Knotts, D.J. (1997) 'Reflection and attentional recovery as distinctive benefits of restorative environments', *Journal of Environmental Psychology*, vol. 17, pp. 165-170.

Hirschi, T. (1969) *Causes of Delinquency*, Berkeley: University of California Press.

HOC (1998) House of Commons, Environment, Transport and Regional Affairs Committee, *The Future for Allotments, Volume 1, Report and Proceedings of the Committee*, HC 560-1.

Hoffman, E. and Castro-Blanco, D. (1988) 'Horticultural therapy with a four-year old boy: a case report', *Journal of Therapeutic Horticulture*, vol. 3, pp. 3-8.

Hoover, R.C. (1994) 'Healing gardens and Alzheimer's disease', in: *The Healing Dimensions of People-Plant Relations*, Francis, M., Lindsey, P. & Rice, J.S. (eds), UC Davis, CA: Center for Design Research, pp. 283-299.

Hyer, L., Boyd, S., Scurfield, R., Smith, D. and Burke, J. (1996) 'Effects of Outward Bound experience as an adjunct to inpatient PTSD treatment of war veterans', *Journal of Clinical Psychology*, vol. 52, (3), pp. 263-278.

Kaiser, M. (1976) 'Alternative to therapy: garden program', *Journal of Clinical Child Psychology*, vol. 5, (2), pp. 21-24.

Kaplan, R. (1973) 'Some psychological benefits of gardening', *Environment and Behavior*, vol. 5, (2), pp. 145-162.

Kaplan, R. (1983) 'The role of nature in the urban context', in: *Human Behavior and Environment: Behaviour and the Natural Environment*, Altman, I. and Wolwill, J.F. (eds), New York: Plenum, vol. 6, pp. 127-161.

Kaplan, S. (1995) 'The restorative benefits of nature: toward an integrative framework', *Journal of Environmental Psychology*, vol. 15, pp. 169-182.

Kaplan, R. and Kaplan, S. (1989) *The Experience of Nature: A Psychological Perspective*, New York: Cambridge University Press.

Kaplan, R. and Kaplan, S. (1990) 'Restorative Experience: the healing power of nearby nature', in: *The Meaning of Gardens*, Francis, M. and Hester, R.T. Jr. (eds), Cambridge, MA: The MIT Press, pp. 238-243.

Kaplan, S. and Talbot, J.F. (1983) 'Psychological benefits of a wilderness experience', in: *Human Behavior and Environment: Behaviour and the Natural Environment*, Altman, I. and Wolwill, J.F. (eds), New York: Plenum, vol. 6, pp. 163-203.

Kay, B.R. (1990) 'Bittersweet Farms', *Journal of Autism and Developmental Disorders*, vol. 20, (3), pp. 309-321.

Kellert, S. R. & Wilson, E.O. (eds) (1993) *The Biophilia Hypothesis*, Washington DC: Island Press.

Kuo, F.E. and Sullivan, W.C. (2001) 'Aggression and violence in the inner city: effects of environment via mental fatigue', *Environment and Behaviour*, vol. 33, (4), pp. 543-571.

Langer, E.J. and Rodin, J. (1976) 'The effects of choice and enhanced personal responsibility for the aged: a field experiment in an institutional setting', *Journal of Personality and Social Psychology*, vol. 34, (2), pp. 191-198.

Lindenmuth, G. F. and Moose, B. (1990) 'Improving cognitive abilities of elderly Alzheimer's patients with intense exercise therapy', *The American Journal of Alzheimer's Care and Related Disorders and Research*, vol. 5, (1), pp. 31-33.

Lloyd, K. (1986) 'The Bec Enterprises workscheme', *British Journal of Occupational Therapy*, vol. 49, (8), pp. 257-258.

Lovering, M. J. (1990) 'Alzheimer's disease and outdoor space: issues in environmental design', *The American Journal of Alzheimer's Care and Related Disorders and Research*, May/June, pp. 33-40.

Markee, K.M. and Janick, J. (1979) 'A bibliography for horticultural therapy (1970-1978): comparison of literature search techniques in an interdisciplinary field', *Horticultural Science*, vol. 14, (6), pp. 692-697.

Maslow, A. H. (1943) 'A theory of human motivation', *Psychological Review*, vol. 50, pp. 370-396.

Maslow, A. H. (1954) *Motivation and Personality*, New York: Harper.

Mather, J. A., Nemecek, D. and Oliver, K. (1997) 'The effect of a walled garden on behavior of individuals with Alzheimer's', *American Journal of Alzheimer's Disease*, vol. 12, (6), pp. 252-257.

Matsuo, E., Fujiki, Y. and Fujiwara, K. (1997) 'Research survey on the therapeutic use of horticulture in welfare institutions and psychiatric hospitals in Fukuoka Prefecture, Japan', *Science Bulletin of the Faculty of Agriculture – Kyushu University*, vol. 52, (1/2), pp. 11-20.

McGinnis, M. (1989) 'Gardening as therapy for children with behavioral disorders', *Journal of Child and Adolescent Psychiatric and Mental Health Nursing*, vol. 2, (3), pp. 87-91.

McGuinn, C. and Relf, P.D. (2001) 'A profile of juvenile offenders in a vocational horticultural curriculum', *HortTechnology*, vol. 11, (3, Jul-Sep), pp. 427-468.

Mooney, P.F. and Milstein, S.L. (1994) 'Assessing the benefits of a therapeutic horticulture program for seniors in intermediate care', in: *The Healing Dimensions of People-Plant Relations*, Francis, M., Lindsey, P. & Rice, J.S. (eds), UC Davis, CA: Center for Design Research, pp. 173-194.

Mooney, P. and Nicell, P.L. (1992) 'The importance of exterior environment for Alzheimer's residents: effective care and risk management', *Health Care Management Forum*, vol. 5, (2), pp. 23-29.

Moore, E.O. (1981) 'A prison environment's effect on health care service demands', *Journal of Environmental Systems*, vol. 11, pp. 17-34.

Neuberger, K.R. (1995) 'Pedagogics and horticultural therapy: the favorite task of Mr. Huber, digging up potatoes', *Acta Horticulturae*, vol. 391, pp. 241-251.

Nixon, B. and Read, S. (1998) 'Therapeutic horticulture for young people with complex mental health problems', in: *Plants and Human Well-being*, Stoneham, J. & Kendle, A (eds), Bath: The Sensory Trust, pp. 67-76.

Olszowy, D.R. (1978) *Horticulture for the Disabled and Disadvantaged*, Springfield, Illinois: Charles C. Thomas.

O'Reilly, P.O. and Handforth, J.R. (1955) 'Occupational therapy with 'refractory' patients', *American Journal of Psychiatry*, vol. 111, pp. 763-766.

Perrins-Margalis, N.M., Rugletic, J., Schepis, N.M., Stepanski, H.R. and Walsh, M.A. (2000) 'The immediate effects of a group-based horticulture experience on the quality of life of persons with chronic mental illness', *Occupational Therapy in Mental Health*, vol. 16, (1), pp. 15-32.

Phillips, D.L. (1967) 'Social participation and happiness', *American Journal of Sociology*, vol. 72, pp. 479-488.

Powch, I.G. (1995) 'Wilderness therapy: what makes it empowering for women?', *Women and Therapy*, vol. 15, (3-4), pp. 11-27.

Prema, T.P., Devarajaiah, C. and Gopinath, P.S. (1986) 'An attempt at Indianisation of psychiatric nursing', *The Nursing Journal of India*, vol. 77, (6), pp. 154-156.

Reeves, C. (1998) 'Horticulture for young people with emotional and behavioural difficulties', in: *The Therapeutic Value of Landscapes*, McDonald, J. & Read, S. (eds), Gillingham: Horticulture for All, pp. 50-62.

Reker, G.T. and Wong, P.T.P. (1988) 'Aging as an individual process: toward a theory of personal meaning', in: *Emergent Theories of Aging, Birren*, J.E. and Bengston, V.L. (Eds), New York: Springer Publishing, pp. 214-246.

Relf, D. (1981) 'Dynamics of horticultural therapy', *Rehabilitation Literature*, vol. 42, (5-6), pp. 147-50.

Reynolds, V. (1999) *The Green Gym: An Evaluation of a Pilot Project in Sonning Common, Oxfordshire*, Report no. 8, Oxford: Oxford Brookes University.

Reynolds, V. (2002) *Well-being Comes Naturally: an Evaluation of the BTCV Green Gym at Portslade, East Sussex*, Report no. 17, Oxford: Oxford Brookes University.

Rice, J.S. and Remy, L.L. (1994.) 'Cultivating self development in urban jail inmates', in: *The Healing Dimensions of People-Plant Relations*, Francis, M., Lindsey, P. & Rice, J.S. (eds), UC Davis, CA: Center for Design Research, pp. 229-256.

Rice, J.S. and Remy, L.L. (1994) 'Evaluating horticultural therapy: the ecological context of urban jail inmates', in: *People-plant relationships: Setting research priorities*, Flagler, J. and Poincelot, R. P. (Eds), New York: The Food Products Press/The Haworth Press, Inc., pp. 203-224.

Rice, J.S.and Remy, L.L. (1998) 'Impact of horticultural therapy on psychosocial functioning among urban jail inmates', *Journal of offender rehabilitation*, vol. 26, (3-4), pp. 169.

Rice, J.S., Remy, L.L. and Whittlesey, L. A. (1998) 'Substance abuse, offender rehabilitation, and horticultural therapy practice', in: *Horticulture as Therapy: Principles and practice*, Simson, S.P. and Straus, M.C. (Eds), New York: The Food Products Press/The Haworth Press, Inc., pp. 257-284.

Richards, H.J. and Kafami, D.M. (1999) 'Impact of horticultural therapy on vulnerability and resistance to substance abuse among incarcerated offenders', *Journal of Offender Rehabilitation*, vol. 29, (3), pp. 183-195.

Rookes, K. (1998) 'Using the school grounds to develop a functional curriculum for children with Autism, restrictive behaviour and severe learning difficulties', in: *The Therapeutic Value of Landscapes*, McDonald, J. & Read, S. (eds), Gillingham: Horticulture for All, pp. 63-72.

Rush, B. (1812) *Medical Inquiries upon Diseases of the Mind*, The History of Medicine Series, No 15, New York: Hafner Publishing Company, (1962).

Russell, K.C. (2001) 'What is wilderness therapy?', *Journal of Experiential Education*, vol. 23, (3), pp. 170-176.

Sarno, M.T. and Chambers, N. (1997) 'A horticultural therapy program for individuals with acquired aphasia', *Activities, Adaptation & Aging*, vol. 22, (1-2), pp. 81-93.

Sarver, M.D. (1985) 'Agritherapy: plants as learning partners', *Academic Therapy*, vol. 20, (4), pp. 389-396.

Schleien, S., Rynders, J., Mustonen, T., Heyne, L. and Kaase, S. (1991) 'Teaching horticultural skills to adults with autism: a replicated case study', *Journal of Therapeutic Horticulture*, vol. 6, (1), pp. 21-37.

Schulz, R. (1976) 'Effects of control and predictability on the physical and psychological well-being of the instituionalized aged', *Journal of Personality and Social Psychology*, vol. 33, (5), pp. 563-573.

Seeman, T. and Chen, X. (2002) 'Risk and protective factors for physical functioning in older adults with and without chronic conditions: MacArthur Studies of Successful Aging', *The Journals of Gerontology, Series B, Psychological Sciences and Socialsciences*, vol. 57, (3), pp. S135-44.

Seller, J., Fieldhouse, J. and Phelan, M. (1999) 'Fertile Imaginations: an inner city allotment group', *Psychiatric Bulletin*, vol. 23, (3), pp. 291-293.

Sharples, A. and Galvin, K (1995) *Evaluation of Cherry Tree Nursery: a Pilot Study by Bournemouth University*, Bournemouth: Bournemouth University.

Shoemaker, C.A., Relf, P.D. and Lohr, V.I. (2000) 'Social science methodologies for studying individuals' responses in human Issues in horticulture research', *HortTechnology*, vol. 10, (1), pp. 87.

Simson, S.,P. & Straus, M.,C. (eds) (1998) *Horticulture as Therapy: Principles and Practice*, Binghamton, NY: The Food Products Press/The Haworth Press, Inc.

Smith, D.J. (1998) 'Horticultural therapy: the garden benefits everyone', *Journal of Psychosocial Nursing and Mental Health Servuices*, vol. 36, (10), pp. 14-21.

Smith, V.D. and Aldous, D.E. (1994) 'Effect of therapeutic horticulture on the self concept of the mildly intellectually disabled student', in: *The Healing Dimensions of People-Plant Relations*, Francis, M., Lindsey, P. & Rice, J.S. (eds), UC Davis, CA: Center for Design Research, pp. 215-221.

Spelfogel, B. and Modrzakowski, M. (1980) 'Curative factors in horticultural therapy in a hospital setting', *Hospital and Community Psychiatry*, vol. 31, (8), pp. 572-573.

Strauss, D. and Gabaldo, M. (1998) 'Traumatic brain injury and horticultural therapy practice', in: *Horticulture as Therapy: Principles and Practice*, Simson, S.P. and Straus, M.C. (Eds), New York: The Food Products Press/The Haworth Press, Inc., pp. 105-129.

Talbott, J., Stern, D., Ross, J. and Gillen, C. (1976) 'Flowering plants as a therapeutic environmental agent in a psychiatric hospital', *HortScience*, vol. 11, (4), pp. 365-366.

Turner, A., Foster, M. and Johnson S.E. (eds) (1996) *Occupational Therapy and Physical Dysfunction: Principles, Skills and Practice*, New York; Edinburgh: Churchill Livingstone.

Ulrich, R.S. (1983) 'Aesthetic and affective response to natural environment', *Human Behaviour and Environment: Behaviour and the Natural Environment*, vol. 6, pp. 85-125, Altman, I and Wohlwill, J.F. (eds), New York: Plenum Press.

Ulrich, R.S (1984) 'View through a window may influence recovery from surgery', *Science*, vol. 224, pp. 420-421.

Ulrich, R.S., Simons, R.F., Losito, B.D., Fiorito, E., Miles, M.A. and Zelson, M. (1991) 'Stress recovery during exposure to natural and urban environments', *Journal of Environmental Psychology*, vol. 11, pp. 201-230.

Unruh, A.M. (1997) 'Spirituality and occupation: garden musings and the Himalayan blue poppy', *Canadian Journal of Occupational Therapy*, vol. 63, pp. 88-94.

Unruh, A. M., Smith, N. and Scammell, C. (2000) 'The occupation of gardening in life-threatening illness: a qualitative pilot project', *Canadian Journal of Occupational Therapy*, vol. 67, (1), pp. 70-77.

Vaccaro, J.V., Cousino, I. and Vatcher, R. (1992) 'The growth of supported employment from horticulture therapy in the veterans' garden', *New Directions for Mental Health Services*, vol. 53, (Spring), pp. 97-104.

Waliczek, T. M., Mattson, R. H. and Zajicek, J. M. (1996) 'Benefits of community gardening on quality-of-life issues', *Journal of Environmental Horticulture*, vol. 14, (4), pp. 204.

Warr, P.B. (1987) *Work, Unemployment and Mental Health*, Oxford: Oxford Science Publications.

Wichrowski, M., Chambers, N.K. and Ciccantelli, L.M. (1998) 'Stroke, spinal cord, and physical disabilities and horticultural therapy practice', in: *Horticulture as Therapy: Principles and Practice*, Simson, S.P. and Straus, M.C. (Eds), New York: The Food Products Press/The Haworth Press, Inc., pp. 71-104.

Williams, B. (2000) 'The treatment of adolescent populations: an institutional vs. a wilderness setting', *Journal of Child and Adolescent Group Therapy*, vol. 10, (1), pp. 47-56.

Williams, S. (1989) 'Evaluation of a horticultural therapy program in a short term psychiatric ward', *Journal of Therapeutic Horticulture*, vol. 4, pp. 29-38.

Wilson, E.O. (1984) Biophilia: *The Human Bond with Other Species*, Cambridge: Harvard University Press.

Winterbottom, D. (1998) 'Casitas, gardens of reclamation: the creation of cultural/social spaces in the barrios of New York City', in: *People, Places and Public Policy*, Sanford, J. and Connell, B.R.(Eds), Edmond, Oklahoma: Environmental Design Research Association, pp. 88-96.

Zhan, L. (1992) 'Quality of life: conceptual and measurement issues', *Journal of Advanced Nursing*, vol. 17, pp. 795-800.

Appendix 1 Databases and search terms

Databases

The following databases were used in the literature search:

ArticleFirst

ASSIA (Applied Social Sciences Index of Abstracts)

BHI (British Humanities Index)

BIDS IBSS

Cambridge Scientific Abstracts/Sociological Abstracts

ECO

INGENTA

Medline

PsychINFO

Web of Science – Science Citation Index; Social Sciences Citation Index

Arts & Humanities Citation Index

WorldCAT

Search Terms

The following terms were used in the search:

Horticulture

Horticultural

Garden(ing)

Community

Disability

Landscape

Health

Therapy

Therapeutic

Rehabilitation

Alzheimer's Disease

Reminiscence

Food AND Meaning

Food AND Growing

Food AND Social

Authors

The following authors' names were used in the search:

Lewis, C.A.

Matsuo, E

Mattson, R.

Relf (P.)D.

Ulrich, R.

Although this list is short these authors have been responsible for a prodigious output of published material in the field of social and therapeutic horticulture and environmental psychology.

The pattern of use of search terms was dependent on the database being searched. For example, using horticultural terms such as "garden", "gardening" or "horticulture" in a medical or psychology database such as Medline or PsychINFO yielded all those publications concerning health aspects of gardening including social and therapeutic horticulture. Relevant articles could easily be selected by examination of the titles. In other databases combinations of terms were used.

Appendix 2 Major conference proceedings and edited texts

There have been a number of international conferences on social and therapeutic horticulture and the proceedings have been published. A number of volumes of edited collections of papers have also been published. Some of the information in these publications has appeared elsewhere, but nonetheless these edited proceedings are a useful and convenient source of information gathered together, as they are, in single volumes. Although many of these have been published in the US they are available from major libraries through the Inter Library Loan scheme and may be purchased from online booksellers such as 'Amazon' who frequently also have used copies for sale.

Conference Proceedings			
	Editors	Title	Publishers
April 19-21, 1990, Arlington, Virginia	Diane Relf	*The Role of Horticulture in Human Well-Being and Social Development: A National Symposium* (published 1992)	Portland, Oregon: Timber Press
March 24-27, 1994, University of California	Mark Francis, Patricia Lindsey, and Jay Stone Rice	*The Healing Dimensions of People-Plant Relations: Proceedings of a Research Symposium*	CA: Center for Design Research, UC Davis
August 22, 1994, Kyoto, Japan	E. Matsuo and P.D. Relf (Diane Relf)	*Horticulture in Human Life, Culture, and Environment*	published as Volume 391 of *Acta Horticulturae*
East Rutherford, NJ, 1994	Joel Flagler and Raymond P. Poincelot	*People Plant Relationships: Setting Research Priorities*	Binghampton, NY: Hayworth Press, Inc.
18 -19 September, 1996, University of Reading, UK[9]	Jane Stoneham and Tony Kendle	*Plants and Human Well-being* (published 1998)	Bath: The Sensory Trust

[9] *Available from: The Sensory Trust, Watering Lane Nursery, Pentewan, Cornwall PL26 6BE*

Conference Proceedings continued...			
	Editors	**Title**	**Publishers**
17 - 18 September 1998, University of Reading, UK[10]	Joanna McDonald and Simon Read	*The Therapeutic Value of Landscapes*	Gillingham: Horticulture for All
September, 2000, University of Nottingham[11]	John Ferris, Mandy Morris, Carol Norman and Joe Sempik	*People, Land & Sustainability: a global view of community gardening* (published 2001)	Nottingham: P.L.S and Co-operative Group ISBN 0-9540408-0-5

Edited Texts			
1990	Mark Francis and Randolph T. Hester, Jr.	*The Meaning of Gardens* (based in part on the Meaning of Gardens Conference, held at the University of California, Davis campus, May 1987)	Cambridge, Mass: The MIT Press
1997	Suzanne E. Wells	*Horticultural Therapy and the Older Adult Population*	*Activities, Adaptation & Aging*, Vol: 22, (1/2)
2000		*International Human Issues in Horticulture*	*HortTechnology*, Vol: 10, (1)
1999	Clare Cooper Marcus and Marni Barnes	*Healing Gardens – Therapeutic Benefits and Design Recommendations*	New York: John Wiley & Sons, Inc.

[10] *Available from: Horticulture for All, Thorngrove Centre, Common Mead Lane, Gillingham, Dorset. SP8 4RE*
[11] *Available from: PLS c/o Humanities Research Centre, Old Engineering Building, University of Nottingham, University Park, Nottingham NG7 2RD*

Appendix 3 Selected instructional texts on social and therapeutic horticulture

		Instructional Texts (Selected)	
1987	Hagedorn, R.	*Therapeutic Horticulture*	Nottingham: Winslow Press
1994	Michael L Hewson	*Horticulture as therapy: a practical guide to using horticulture as a therapeutic tool*	Guelph, Ontario: Greenmor Printing Company Limited
1998	Sharon Pastor Simson, and Martha C. Straus (Eds).	*Horticulture as therapy: Principles and practice*	Binghamton, NY: The Food Products Press/The Haworth Press, Inc, ISBN 1560228598
1998	Martha M. Tyson	*The Healing Landscapes: Therapeutic Outdoor Environments*	McGraw-Hill Companies, Inc ISBN 0070657688
2001	Donald Norfolk	*The Therapeutic Garden*	Bantam Press ISBN 0593045017